Out-Island D

LINE DRAWINGS BY GUY FLEMING

Out-Island Doctor

by Evans W. Cottman

WITH WYATT BLASSINGAME

Hodder & Stoughton

LONDON SYDNEY AUCKLAND TORONTO

British Library Cataloguing in Publication Data

Cottman, Evans W.
 Out-island doctor.
 1. Medicine—Bahamas
 I. Title   II. Blassingame, Wyatt
 610'.92'4   R475.B24

 ISBN 0-340-39869-8

Dedicated to my friend and mentor,
Dr. Charles Maxwell-Joyner, who has
helped make this book possible, through
his patient effort to indoctrinate
me in the art of medical practice.

CONTENTS

MAPS

Out-Island Doctor

1

"De Doctuh Done Reach"

WE made quite a procession along the single, unpaved street of True Blue, Crooked Island, The Bahamas.

First there was the colored constable in his white uniform, stopping in front of each house to blow his whistle and shout, "De doctuh done reach! De doctuh done reach!" I came next, barefooted, wearing torn shorts and a T shirt long since gone dark with sweat and dust, and leading Shadow, a sway-backed sorrel so loaded with my drugs, medical instruments, bedding, and drinking water there was no room for me. After Shadow came most of the native population of True Blue, a cheering, impromptu parade, literally throwing their hats in the air and echoing the constable's shout, "De doctuh done reach!" For though the news had quickly outrun the procession, the constable continued to stop before every house, blast on his whistle, and make his proclamation.

About halfway down the street he turned to face me. "Here, Doctuh," he said, "is the home of Miss Daisy Nottage where we have fixed a place for you, where you can see your patients and sleep at night."

It was 4 in the afternoon and I had walked thirty miles since morning. I told the constable I would like to rest a few minutes before starting work. "Yes indeed, Doctuh," he said. "You mus' rest first, and I'll keep the folks away while you do." Then he added, "But there is plenty plenty peoples waitin' to see you. Dey been prayin' long time for you to come."

"Give me thirty minutes," I said.

3

I was shown to my room and lay down. But through the walls I could hear the murmur of the crowd and the constantly repeated question, "When de doctuh goin' see de peoples?" followed by the constable's adamant answer, "He tired now. He see you later."

I was new at the practice of medicine and comparatively new in the islands. I had come to True Blue expecting to attend to a half dozen, perhaps a dozen patients, get a night's sleep, and start walking back across the island next morning. But judging from the sounds outside, I was going to have far more work than I had expected. Wearily I got up, opened the door, and told the constable to send in the first patient.

She was a ten-year-old girl with a dislocated knee. Her father carried her into the room, followed by as many other persons as could jam their way through the door. Big-eyed, silent, they watched me kneel in front of the girl and touch her knee.

It was a tense moment in True Blue—tense for all of us. Quite possibly, I was the first doctor many of these persons had ever seen. On my part, this was the first time I had ever been confronted with a dislocated knee. Moreover, I was not really a doctor in the accepted sense of the word—not an M.D., but merely a layman who had found himself plunged suddenly into an overwhelming and sometimes terrifying situation. Now, as I began to manipulate the child's leg, I was probably as frightened as my patient.

I was also lucky. Almost instantly the bone snapped into place. The child gave a short cry and stood up. She took two steps away from her father, limping, but walking for the first time in days. When she stopped she looked up at me, a huge grin spreading slowly across her face.

In the room there was a long moment of stunned silence. Then an awed voice whispered, "What is dis?"

"It's a miracle!"

"Dot one wunnerful mon!"

"Praise de Lawd!"

I was aware that within the space of seconds I had, however

5

unjustifiably, been elevated to the rank of the gods. It was a flattering sensation, but it didn't lessen the work ahead or the crowd in the room. Everybody still outside was now trying to jam inside to see "de miracle." I had to tell the constable it was impossible to work under such conditions. Besides, some of the patients would want privacy.

I got instant cooperation. The constable put on his official cap, blew his whistle, and declaimed, "How de doctuh goin' to work with all you peoples in here? Plenty womens wants to see de doctuh private. Now everybody go outside and wait until he calls you." He blew his whistle again and the crowd filed out.

I did my best. I worked until dark, ate a sandwich from my paper bag, and kept working. I pulled teeth, prescribed for indigestion and assorted other ills, disinfected and bandaged a wide variety of injuries. At midnight there were still ten persons waiting and I was too exhausted to trust my judgment any longer. I told them to come back early the next morning. I could finish with them by 10 o'clock, I thought, and start the long walk back across the island.

It seemed I had scarcely lain down when the noise awoke me. It was daylight and somebody was knocking on the door. Still half asleep, I stumbled across the room and looked out. The yard was filled with people. There were at least twenty of them, and the sun not yet clear of the horizon. A very dark old lady beamed happily at me. "We come early, Doctuh, like you say."

I asked for time to wash my face. I ate another sandwich, took a long pull on my bottle of drinking water, and went to work. I worked all morning and at noon the crowd was bigger than it had been at dawn. By now the news of my presence had spread to the nearby settlements of Brown, Bullet Hill, and Thompson's Creek. Everybody was making haste to get to a doctor while the getting was good.

The afternoon came and went, with the end nowhere in sight. Again I worked until midnight and sent would-be patients home with instructions to be back early in the morning.

I had eaten no dinner or supper, partially because of lack of time and partially because I now had only one sandwich left. Food is always a problem in the out-islands where stores and restaurants are almost nonexistent and where the natives live largely on hard-cooked grits and dried fish, sometimes cooked beneath an abundant swarm of flies. I broke my sandwich in half, and the last I remember was sitting down on the side of the bed to eat it.

Then it was daylight again with patients knocking on the door. But this time the crowd was not as big as it had been. I ate the final half of my sandwich with a feeling the end of my labors was in sight. And true enough, by noon the slate was clean.

Since there was nothing left to eat I lost no time on dinner. I packed as fast as possible, piled all the gear on Shadow, thanked Miss Daisy Nottage for the use of her cottage, and departed. But within half an hour I heard running footsteps behind me. It was a small boy. "Doctuh," he panted, "you must come back. Peoples over to Acklins just hear you is come, and plenty now comin' to you from Lovely Bay and Chester."

I was half starved and completely worn out. Besides, there would be patients waiting for me at the village of Church Grove where I had left fresh medical supplies—and food— and where I was supposed to have returned two days before. So I told the boy I was very sorry, but I would have to see the people from Acklins on my next trip. "Right now," I said, "I have an urgent call to go to Church Grove."

It was no lie. The way I looked at it, both the waiting patients and my own hunger constituted an urgent call.

It was well after dark when I reached Church Grove. As a village, it was not much bigger than True Blue, but I kept an office of sorts there. I was unloading Shadow in the yard when Mistress Bain, who lived next door and took care of the place for me, came running out. She was weeping so desperately I had some trouble understanding what had happened.

It seemed that after I left for True Blue she had hung my

bedding out to air, then, going back for it a couple of hours later, she found the blanket missing. Appalled, she was about to accuse the village one and all of theft when her donkey came around the corner of the house. "And, Doctuh, one corner of de blanket was hangin' out his mouth. I run quick and grab it, but de donkey swallow harder'n I can pull. All de blanket went inside. Den de donkey get sick, and you don't come back, and today he dead."

I consoled her as best I could, then staggered wearily inside to cook my supper and lie down upon my blanketless bed. If I had not been too tired to ponder on anything, it would have been a good time to ponder on the quirks of fate and human nature that had brought me to these islands and converted me, if not into a doctor, then into an "unqualified practitioner" with a practice that was truly incredible, in more ways than one.

2

Gypsy Blood

I suppose the logical place to start is the very beginning.

I was born, early in the century and late in the year, in Indianapolis. My father was a historian and writer, with several books to his credit. He also was cursed with a dash of the gypsy. My mother, a woman of refinement and education, preferred to stay at home. This made for certain conflicts which may, or may not, have influenced the course of my own life. My childhood was spent, rather uneventfully, in Indianapolis. Butler University gave me an A.B., and later a Master's degree in biochemistry. In 1925 I was appointed teacher of sciences in the high school at Madison, Indiana.

I held the job for twenty years. I brought my mother and

father—mother had won the travel arguments—to live with me. Later we were joined by my Aunt Mabel Tibbott, my mother's unmarried sister. I was honestly devoted to all of them. I believe I did fairly well as a teacher, and I believe my students would agree on that. I also suspect that both students and faculty pretty much considered me to be the eternal bachelor, destined to teach quietly in Madison from then until my personal doomsday. It would have been the natural conclusion to reach.

There was, however, another less obvious side of my nature. Even as a child I hated Indiana winters. When other children were out romping in the snow, I sat huddled over the register, reading books. As I grew older my dislike for cold weather increased. Some of my father's dammed-up gypsy blood flowed in my veins, its influence more and more dominant. I became haunted by vague yearnings to break away from restraint, to visit new and strange places and do new things.

I continued to teach, but by 1937 there was an idea firmly fixed in my mind. In 1945 I would be eligible for a small pension. It would amount to $28.63 a month. But I was saving money; I had a little; I could make out. In 1945 I was going to quit teaching, go south—it had to be south—to some strange, enchanting, little-known island, and carve out a new career for myself. What that career would be I had no idea and didn't much care. But it wouldn't be teaching.

The next step was to find the place. I ransacked the local libraries, devouring everything I could find about tropical and subtropical places, gradually eliminating those that would not suit my purpose. Some were too intensely hot; I didn't like cold, but I didn't want to be scorched either. Some were too infested with malaria and other tropical diseases; I yearned for adventure, but not that kind. Also, I wanted a place close enough so I could make a fairly extensive trial visit during a summer vacation. The Bahamas sounded like a natural and I began to read everything about them I could find.

The Bahamas lie off the coast of Florida and are easily accessible. The climate is subtropical, tempered by the Gulf

Stream, delightful both winter and summer. There is a minimum of tropical disease. The majority of the population—on many islands the entire population—is colored, the descendants of former slaves. The white minority is largely made up of the descendants of former Loyalists who fled there from the States during or soon after the Revolution. The capital, Nassau, is located on New Providence Island and is the only city. All the other islands—and there are literally thousands of them—are called "out-islands." Some of these are uninhabited, some dotted with tiny villages or "settlements." I decided I wanted to visit the out-islands.

I discovered a prize in the Indiana State Library: a *Year Book of the Bahamas*, giving the names and addresses of the out-island commissioners. In the spring of 1939 I began a letter-writing campaign, asking for information, saying I wanted to visit the islands during the coming summer, and possibly settle there a few years later.

The answers were prompt and interesting. I was particularly intrigued by letters from a Mr. E. W. Forsyth, commissioner of Andros Island, and a Mr. Herman Pyfrom, commissioner of the Long Cay district. The Long Cay district, Mr. Pyfrom said, included Acklins and Crooked Island as well as Long Cay, and he wrote delightfully of the beauty of the area and the simple life of the natives. Mr. Forsyth told me he had been commissioner of Andros for almost forty years and his letter revealed an intense love of the place. He also mentioned a Mr. Percy Cavill, a former swimming champion said to have invented the Australian Crawl, who was currently living in retirement on Andros.

I laid my plans to visit Andros and Long Cay that summer. I wrote both the commissioners, and both replied promptly. Since I had so few out-island contacts, I also wrote to Mr. Percy Cavill, saying I planned to be in Andros about June 4 and hoped to meet him. He did not answer; so I concluded Mr. Cavill was not too keen on uninvited visitors, and forgot him.

3

Of Mangoes, Sailboats, and Mr. Percy Cavill's Missing Bladder

At 1 p.m. on May 29, 1939, the Madison, Indiana, high school closed for the summer. At 1:15 p.m. I was on a bus bound for Miami. Three days later I was flying from Miami to Nassau.

One thing of importance had occurred in the meanwhile.

From the letters of Mr. Forsyth and Mr. Pyfrom I had gathered that travel in the out-islands was sometimes a bit crude. So when I left home I was carrying a very old and battered suitcase which I figured nothing could hurt. In Miami I stepped off the bus into a thunderstorm—and the suitcase disintegrated.

Looking for a replacement, I soon found the cheap ones were too cheap—one rain and they too would vanish—while the expensive ones were too expensive. Finally I was hit with an idea. I located a feed store (not an easy thing to do in Miami) and for five cents bought a large burlap bag (a croaker sack, the salesman called it), stuffed my clothing into this, and tied the end with a string. When I caught the plane out of Miami I had this thrown over one shoulder. Perhaps it was not exactly chic; but it fitted the dream I had dreamed between classes in Madison. It made me, I hoped, look faintly like Long John Silver climbing the gangplank of the *Hispaniola*. . . . I might add that it proved to be the most practical piece of luggage I have ever carried.

The flight from Miami to Nassau was my first time on an airplane, and I doubt if there is a more beautiful place in the world to make a first flight. The Gulf Stream was a vast and slightly rumpled indigo blanket, flecked now and then with platinum where a wave crested into foam. Beyond this were the shallows, the water changing through every possible shade of blue and green and silver. I had never seen such colors. I could scarcely believe them. The drab corridors of Madison High School seemed a world away.

Indeed, Nassau then was like part of another planet. I took a horse-drawn taxi from the airport and at first I was aware only of a jumble of impressions: Old-World houses framed in flaming tropical gardens, street vendors with baskets on their heads, calling musical words I could only partially understand, the dock with sailboats tied alongside. And always, in the background, the vivid tropical sea.

Marjorie Rawlings once wrote, "There is an affinity between people and places. . . . If there be any such thing as racial memory, the consciousness of land and water must lie deeper in the core of us than any knowledge of our fellow beings. . . . And along with that deep knowledge of the earth is a preference of each of us for certain kinds of it." I had found my preference.

At the Bahamas Development Board a very gracious young lady told me I could get a nice, reasonably priced room at the home of Miss Taylor, 49 Charlotte Street. I asked if she could give me the address of Mr. Forsyth, the Andros Island commissioner. "Oh," she said, "when Mr. Forsyth is in Nassau he lives at Miss Taylor's. I think he is there now."

He was, a tall, sparsely built, deeply tanned man in his mid sixties but with the energy and enthusiasm of a teen-ager. He gave me a most cordial welcome and started immediately to tell me about Andros. It is the largest of the Bahamas with an area of some 1600 square miles. Mr. Forsyth's office was on a section known as Mangrove Cay; there was no hotel but he had a cottage there and insisted I was welcome to use it. He wrote a note for me to give to his housekeeper, Lucy. Then he told me the mailboat had already left for Andros and there would not be another for two weeks. However, the *Clipper K*, a local sailboat, was going in three days. He could arrange passage for me, if I wished.

That gave me three splendid days in Nassau, and I spent them in a daze—walking, riding the horse-drawn taxis, trying to get used to British money, and on one occasion trying to learn to eat a mango. I bought this from a native fruit vendor because it looked pretty. When I asked what it was she said something that sounded like *mahn gaw*. If she had said *mango* it would not have helped: in Indiana a mango is a stuffed green pepper. This one, the vendor told me, grew on a tree.

There was an elaborate financial transaction, conducted on my part on sheer faith: I gave her a piece of paper money of uncertain denomination and got back a handful of coins. Then I took the mango to Miss Taylor's, washed it carefully, and bit into it.

Quickly I realized that this was not the procedure. The skin was tough and bitter and the juice ran over my hands instead of into my mouth. I took a knife and tried to cut through it, to eat from the inside out. There was a seed in the middle, and the seed and fruit refused to part company. Meanwhile the juice was flowing in small rivers down my chin, throat, hands, and arms. It seemed impossible such a flood of juice could come from one fruit. I rushed to the bathroom and, standing in the tub, managed to eat most of the mango, though not before I was pretty well smeared with juice. It was delicious. But I still believe the only neat way to eat a mango is to do it while swimming.

The *Clipper K* was to sail at 6 o'clock in the afternoon and I arrived at the dock early, carrying my gunnysack luggage. This was to be my first trip on a sailing ship, and as I looked the situation over I began to have doubts.

The *Clipper K*, Mr. Forsyth had told me, was a large sloop.

13

I didn't know what a sloop was; but I had been dreaming vaguely of Moby Dick and four-masted, square-rigged sailing ships. The *Clipper K* had one mast and, when I came on the dock, no sail at all that I could see. It had a crew of four, all very big and all very dark, stripped to the waist and, at the time of my arrival, very busy. They shouted at one another in that strange Bahamian accent, part British and part native, and they used terms that had no meaning to me. Their faces were somber and forbidding. I thought of being alone with them on the wine-dark sea. I thought of the fact that I had money with me, more money than I would ever normally carry back in Madison. Once out of sight of land these men might easily rob me, throw me overboard. They could say I had fallen in the sea; no one would ever know.

"All right, boss," the captain said. "You could come aboard now."

I stepped on deck. The lines to the dock were thrown off. One man began to pull on a rope and slowly a great white sail unfurled. The wind shook it. Here was the first touch of the beauty I had always associated with sailboats, and I watched fascinated.

One of the crew said, "Watch de boom, boss."

I wasn't quite sure I understood him. I looked around, wondering what I was supposed to watch, and where. Perhaps there was some kind of parting salute to be fired. Other boats had left the dock with no guns fired; but then I was a visitor from another country—I had been brought to the dock by the commissioner of Andros. Maybe— About that time the wind caught the sail; it and the great heavy timber fastened to it, the boom, swung across the boat, missing my head by inches.

"Bossman," the captain said, "I think you best go below till we gets clear."

At least I had some idea what "below" meant, and I went.

The cook followed me in a few minutes. From a cupboard he took flour and water and started to make a round loaf of dough. I asked what it was. "Dis moonbread," he said. "We calls it moonbread because it so round, like the moon. Some

15

folks calls it johnnycake." He stirred up a little fire and put the bread in a small Dutch oven. "Is you an American?"

I told him I was. He asked, "Does you know President Roosevelt?"

"Oh yes," I said. "All Americans know President Roosevelt."

He stuck his head out of the cabin and called to the others, "De bossman say he knows President Roosevelt." This brought exclamations of astonishment and what sounded like approval. One after another the crew came to the door to look at me for a moment, then vanish again.

I hadn't intended to lie to them, but neither did I want to change any erroneous impressions my answer might have created. Maybe they'll be a little more careful how they rob and murder a friend of FDR's, I thought.

When the moonbread was done I asked to sample it. I was hungry and it tasted good. Also, apparently, moonbread was to be the only dinner served.

This did not bother me for long. The breeze freshened and the boat began to roll. Inside my stomach things began to roll also, with a strange uncertainty. I went out and lay down on deck. It was dark now, nothing visible but sea and stars and the big sail overhead. I wanted to enjoy the beauty and the romance of it all. I wanted to stand on the bow with the wind in my face and sing. Instead I lay on the deck and held my stomach with both hands.

It was my first attack of seasickness, and quite truly I was ashamed of it. I tried to hide it from the crew. I was no longer worried about being murdered—I was just beginning to hope I would be—but I was sure that to these men seasickness would be a sign of almost contemptible weakness, or at the best an hilarious joke. So I lay there and fought the inevitable —and lost the battle, along with the moonbread.

Quickly the crew gathered around, but not to make jokes. "You is seasick! What a pity," the captain said in honest sympathy. "Take a little sea water in your hand and drink it. It

16

will strengthen your stomach." I tried it, scooping up a small swallow in the palm of one hand. And it did help. One of the crew brought out a blanket and covered me with it, tucking it carefully around my feet.

I looked up at them in gratitude. I was aware of the brotherhood of man. But I still was not up to enjoying my first night on a tropic sea. Instead, I fell into an uneasy sleep.

It must have been about 2 A.M. when I awoke suddenly. The boat was shaking all over, the sail trembling violently. I jumped up. There was only one man visible, sitting at the helm.

"What's the matter?" I called. "Is it a hurricane?"

"O no, suh," he said calmly. "We just lay to day clean."

I didn't have any idea what he meant; but certainly he wasn't excited. So I lay down again and went to sleep. Later I would learn that whenever native boatmen approach the dangerous Andros reef at night they lay to: that is, turn head on into the wind, which stops the boat but makes the sails flap. And in the Andros dialect "day clean" means "daybreak."

So at "day clean" the *Clipper K* got under way again going cautiously inside a coral reef and onto a calm, blue-green lagoon. Ahead of us was Mangrove Cay, but there was no dock visible, just a long stretch of white sand and behind that a grove of coconut palms. Here and there among the palms I could see a small house, but that was all.

We anchored about two hundred yards offshore. A dinghy was put over the side. The captain climbed into it; my luggage was handed to him, and I followed. There were no seats in the dinghy. I sat on my gunnysack suitcase while the captain sculled, pushing the long oar that hung over the stern away from him with one hand, pulling it back against his chest with the other. It was the first time I had ever seen a boat sculled and for a few moments I watched fascinated. Then I forgot it in staring at the island ahead.

There is no tree more graceful than the coconut palm. At Mangrove Cay the grove ran along the beach as far as the eye

17

could see. Here and there among the trees a footpath curved and vanished, a hibiscus blossom would explode against the lacy shade.

The dinghy scraped bottom. I was barefooted. I jumped over the side and waded ashore through the warm water.

And then to add to the picture a man came out of the palm trees. He was wearing a pair of old shorts and no shirt. He was tall, powerfully built, sunburned to the color of a well-smoked briar pipe. He was past sixty, but his muscles were as flat and hard as those of a twenty-year-old athlete. He extended his hand. "Evans Cottman, I presume?"

I stared at him. "Yes . . ."

"Cavill's my name. I got your letter a few months ago, but I didn't worry to answer it. Letters give me the writer's cramp. You're right on time, I see. I just got here myself a little while ago. I've been sailing all night from Madeira Cay to get here to meet you."

This all left me slightly bewildered. It was true (though I had forgotten it until that moment) that several months before I had written Mr. Percy Cavill saying I hoped to reach Andros sometime around the fourth of June. But the fact I had arrived on that exact day was pure luck. When I mentioned this he waved one hand. "Quite all right. I knew you were coming; talked to Forsyth about it a while back. If you hadn't showed up today, I could have waited around. Time doesn't mean much out here. Where are you going to stay?"

I told him of Mr. Forsyth's kind offer.

He shook his head. "You won't have any company at Mangrove Cay. Better come out to my place and we'll sail, fish, swim, anything you like."

Despite the fact he had not answered my letter, I had hoped to meet Cavill. In Nassau Mr. Forsyth had spoken of him as a picturesque character, an Australian, a former professional athlete who had sort of gone native on Andros. He was supposed to know the district as well as any white man alive. So now I jumped at the chance to visit him.

He showed me the way to Forsyth's house where I presented my letter to Lucy, the housekeeper, and explained that I was going to stay with Mr. Cavill. She seemed unhappy to lose a guest, but fixed us an excellent lunch. As we were about to leave, Cavill crawled under the house and pulled out a plank about eight inches wide and eighteen feet long. He was carrying it to the beach when Lucy came flying out of the house behind us.

"Hey, Mr. Cavill, Mr. Forsyth want dot board!" she screamed.

Cavill merely waved. "It's all right. Tell him I needed it." He did not say what for. Lucy stayed where she was, looking darkly after us and muttering.

Cavill's sailboat was anchored just off the beach. We waded out to it, carrying the board, my gunnysack, a bag of groceries Cavill had bought at the local store, and two bags of straw he had somehow acquired. When everything was aboard he told me, "You take the tiller while I get the sail up."

"Take what?" I asked.

"The tiller."

He pointed toward the stern. On the seat there was a large conch shell. I picked it up and held it toward him. "Is this what you mean?"

For a moment he looked as puzzled as I was. Then he started to roar. He had a laugh that shook him from his heels up. "You've never been in a sailboat?" he asked finally.

"Not before last night."

He took hold of the steering stick. "Allow me to introduce you to the tiller. And if you stay in the islands you'll get better acquainted. Now hold on and do as I tell you."

I held the tiller, somewhat cautiously, while he got the sail up. The boat began to move. "Hard down," Cavill said. I pushed down on the tiller, hard. It wouldn't budge. "Keep off!" he called, and pointed to the right. I pushed the tiller to the right. And the boat instantly turned to the left. It stopped, sail flapping.

19

Cavill rocked with laughter, but it was friendly laughter. He took over, got the boat under way alone, and as we sailed he began to tell me about himself.

He had been born in Sydney, Australia, where his father owned a bathing beach. As a boy Percy's job had been to dive under the dock each spring and bare-handed clean out the octopi which lived there. If he didn't get them all, his father beat him. After one such beating, at the age of sixteen, Percy stowed away on a ship bound for San Francisco. There he dived overboard and swam ashore. His future wanderings took him around the world a half dozen times. He had worked at anything and everything. He had invented the Australian Crawl and had won more medals than he could remember. During the Florida boom he had been swimming instructor at one of Carl Fisher's swank Miami Beach hotels and accumulated a good bit of money.

In later years hard times hit him. He began to drink. He sold off his trophies one by one. Finally he had come to the Bahamas and built a shack on one of the Andros cays called Steamer Cay. A hurricane washed the shack away and he spent three days clinging to a half-submerged tree. It was after this, he told me, he had moved to Madeira Cay because it had higher ground and there built a new home. I asked if he'd had hurricane insurance on the first home, but the only answer I got was another howl of laughter.

With a fair wind driving us along we reached Cavill's cay in about two hours. It was a tiny island, like a dozen others we had passed. Mangroves walled a little inlet, but in one place there was a small strip of beach and just back of this a low hill with a little house on top of it.

"Here we are," Cavill said.

We anchored and waded ashore carrying our supplies. A path wound up the hill through a maze of scrubby bushes. At the top was a clearing with a pathetic little garden at the forward end: some parched and worm-eaten cabbages, tomatoes, a few plants I didn't recognize. Beyond the garden was a small yard littered with a fantastic collection of odds and ends: broken tree limbs and bits of firewood, parts of an ancient automobile motor, empty oil tins, a Dutch oven; a net hung from a nearby tree, a fish spear stuck upright in the ground. Near this a hole had been dug. It was evidently some kind of garbage pit for it was half filled with small, amazingly white, polished bones.

Beyond this was the house. It was (I measured it later) exactly nine feet wide by twenty-one feet long. The walls were of clapboard, the roof thatched with palm fronds. Cavill pushed the sagging door open with his foot—and instantly a large black hen rushed out between his legs, followed by a saucy little Dominic rooster. "Come in," Cavill said. "Drop your gear anywhere."

The inside was, if possible, more disorderly than the outside. The floor was of naked, hard-packed coral earth, with empty boxes and tin pans and tools of various sorts scattered everywhere. Against one wall was a table made of planks placed across two upended boxes. On it were more pans, unwashed dishes, an ancient kerosene lantern, and a lamp with a dirty chimney. Cavill's bed was an ancient affair with a high iron headboard, the straw mattress only partially covered by a crumpled blanket. Underneath the bed was a hen's nest. This was of straw, very carefully fashioned. It was, I think, the neatest thing in the room.

Cavill bent down and took an egg from the nest. "She rarely misses a day," he said happily. There was a cupboard nailed against one wall and he opened this and put the egg carefully inside. "I'm saving them for her to set."

With the egg out of the way he looked around and located a saw under the table. With this he cut the plank he had brought from Mr. Forsyth's into three six-foot lengths. He found two boxes of approximately the same height and put the planks on them. Then he took the two bags of straw he'd brought and spread this on the planks. For a moment he regarded the result of his work solemnly before he said, not looking at me, "Did you happen to bring a blanket of some sort?"

I assured him I had. "Good!" he said. "I'm a bit short at the moment. But now you'll be comfortable."

He seemed more sure of that than I was.

The cooking (we had moonbread and boiled fish for supper) was done outside, but we ate inside at the table. Just as we sat down the hen flew up to roost for the night on a rafter directly over my head. I shifted uneasily. Cavill was carefully picking the bones from his fish and telling me at the same time about an operation he had once undergone. "Doctor took out my bladder," he said, chewing steadily. "After I was feeling a bit better he brought it in to show me. I wanted to keep it, a kind of souvenir you know, but he wouldn't leave it. Couple of days later I found out why. I looked out the window and there he was in the yard blowing up my bladder to have a game of touch football with the nurses."

Over my head the hen made a soft, sleepy noise. I stood up quickly and moved her about two feet down the rafter. "What's the trouble?" Cavill asked with mock indignity. "Don't you trust my hen? I've taught her to be a lady."

About that time we smelled smoke. "Oh, the moonbread!" he said. "I forgot it." He ran out and came back with a half-charred loaf and threw it on the floor in disgust. Then he emptied his plate of fishbones beside it.

I suppose my face showed my thoughts because he started to laugh. "Don't worry. It's quite sanitary. The ants will have them clean as a whistle by morning."

I picked up the plates and carried them down to the bay. While I was scouring them with sand Cavill appeared.

"You're the worst old maid I ever saw," he said, chuckling. "You're going to scrub holes in my plates. I never wash them."

"You mean the ants clean them as well as the bones?"

"Of course."

I figured it was not my duty as guest to argue with him. But I went right ahead and scrubbed the plates.

We turned in early, and I was so completely exhausted my bed felt almost comfortable. For just a few minutes. At this

22

point the breeze that had been blowing quit. Within seconds every exposed part of my body was covered by something that felt like sparks. I began to slap violently, and hit nothing. I thought of Cavill's ants gnawing the bones on the floor. I thought of them cleaning the flesh from my bones the way he claimed they cleaned the plates.

"Sand flies," Cavill said in the darkness. "We'll have 'em until the breeze starts again."

He got up and lit the lamp. Even then I could not see what was stinging me, but I could feel. It was like being stabbed with red-hot but invisible needles.

Meanwhile Cavill was rounding up some odd scraps and building a small fire in a weird tin contraption on the floor. Then he smothered the fire with leaves until it gave off a dense, acrid smoke. The smoke got rid of the sand flies, but it burned my eyes, nose, and throat.

Cavill had blown out the lamp and gone back to bed. "Don't have them often," he said. "Just when the wind stops. Nuisance when we do, though." He began to snore.

I lay there, alternately strangling on the smoke and being burned alive when it cleared. Under such circumstances it is difficult to be philosophical and soul-searching. But I tried. I wondered what I was doing here on an island I had never even heard of twelve hours before. Had I simply been fleeing the crummy corridors of Madison High School? Or searching in stupidity for something that didn't exist? Or did I actually enjoy being eaten alive by invisible insects with red-hot teeth?

I arrived at no conclusion. As suddenly as it had ceased, the breeze sprang up again. The smoke cleared. The sand flies vanished. I could hear the long soft sighing of the surf a hundred feet away. I could hear the wind in the coconut palms. The night was delightfully cool and I slept like a baby.

Next morning the ants had cleaned and polished the fishbones on the floor just as Cavill had said they would, and he swept them out the door into the nearby pothole. The ants, however, had not bothered the charred moonbread. Wrapped half around it was a gigantic centipede at least nine inches

23

long. It seemed sluggish and Cavill remarked that it was probably suffering from indigestion.

Because I wanted to count its legs and see if it really had one hundred, we put it in a fruit jar where it could be examined from all angles. But if there were more than forty-four legs I couldn't find them. With that settled, Cavill called his two chickens and threw the centipede to them. The rooster backed away. The black hen, however, quickly maneuvered for position. Amazingly fast, she would peck the centipede, drop it before it could strike back, then peck it again. Finally it was broken and dead.

At this point the rooster stepped up and took possession. The hen backed away, and the rooster ate the whole thing.

"There's a moral there," Cavill said. "Only I'm not sure just what it is."

We went for a swim. I had learned the Australian Crawl back in the States, but Cavill was horrified with my execution. He was giving me instruction when a creature about three feet long came swimming past. "Shark," Cavill said.

At this point I put the swimming lesson into violent practice and hit the beach so fast I almost skidded up it. When I looked back Cavill was standing just where he had been, shaking with laughter. "You ought to be giving me lessons!" he shouted. "I never saw anybody before could swim fifty yards without touching the water with anything but their fingertips."

"The shark?" I asked.

"It was a baby. It was more afraid than you were." He began to laugh again. "No," he said. "I don't think it could have been."

Next morning Cavill said he was going to take me to visit a Captain Rees. The Captain, he explained, was a retired aide-de-camp of King George V and a holder of the Victoria Cross, won for gallantry as a pilot in World War I. Sometime in the 1930's Rees had bought a twenty-nine-foot yacht and set out to cross the Atlantic alone. Originally he aimed for New York, but at that latitude the prevailing winds were against him. When his motor conked out before he had gone 500 miles, he

24

hoisted sail, turned south almost a thousand miles to catch the trade winds, rode out a hurricane, and eventually landed in the Bahamas. He liked them so well he stayed on. At present he was living on his boat in a small cove about four miles from Cavill's.

We went in Cavill's sailboat, winding between a myriad of tiny uninhabited islands. Captain Rees was anchored off one of these called Mastic Cay. Mastic Cay, Cavill told me, belonged to Mr. Forsyth, and although there was no house on it, it had been planted with fruit trees and flowers until the island bloomed like a tropical garden. Rees's white yacht in the cove made the picture complete.

The Captain was a big, rawboned Welshman; and if he deliberately lived a solitary life he made up for it when he had company. He was talking before we came alongside and he could get in more words per minute than a speed reader. He clipped the last syllable, or syllables, off most of them, and he spoke the others in such a Welsh accent that I could understand only half of what he said. But obviously Cavill and I were welcome.

I never really appreciated the meaning of the word "shipshape" until I stepped on Captain Rees's boat. The cabin space was tiny, with every inch of it fitted to maximum use. There was a place for everything, and everything was exactly in its place. There was even a miniature machine shop with a lathe, on which Rees, still talking, turned out a new pipe stem to replace the one Cavill had broken.

The Captain invited us to stay for dinner and we happily accepted, there being no other place we could eat without sailing back to Cavill's. The food was bully beef out of a can, but the service was something else again. The Captain brought out a complete set of sterling silver, each piece bearing the Rees coat of arms, and set to work polishing it. Meanwhile he talked, mixing a wild collection of ancient British jokes with personal anecdotes about people he referred to only by their first names. It was a long time before I realized he was talking about various members of the British royal family.

Then, with the bully beef ready and the silver set, Captain Rees dressed for dinner. That is, he changed his torn shorts for an immaculate white pair. Perhaps in deference to his underdressed guests he did not add a shirt or shoes.

It was night when Cavill and I left. There was a moon and it made our sail look milk-white and very clean. The wake of the boat was milky. The little islands to right and left were dark, with now and then a tall palm outlined against the sky. A porpoise rolled alongside us and made a blowing noise and went away. I thought of Captain Rees's formal dinners at Buckingham Palace, and of Percy Cavill being whipped for leaving an octopus under an Australian dock, and of Evans Cottman teaching first-year biology to bored students in Madison, Indiana—and now the three of us meeting on an otherwise uninhabited island in the Bahamas.

It seemed like a very strange and wonderful thing that could only happen in a strange and wonderful country. And I had the feeling that if I could manage to see more of the country, even more strange and wonderful things would happen.

4

"We Have Prepared a Place of Honor for You"

I WAS able to devote only six weeks to my initial trip to the Bahamas, and so had allotted approximately two weeks each for visits to Andros, the Windward Islands, and Abaco. Consequently, when I got a chance to return to Nassau a few days after meeting Captain Rees, I somewhat reluctantly took it. From Nassau, on the twentieth of June, I caught the mail-boat for Long Cay.

On most charts Long Cay is shown as Fortune Island, though very few Bahamians know it by that name. It is, normally, about a three-day sail from Nassau. On this occasion the water was rough and I was seasick most of the time. The mailboat was crowded; there was a cruise party aboard and those who weren't seasick were drunk.

Personally, I don't drink. My father was a strong temperance man; my mother, a veritable pillar in the WCTU. I was brought up in the way I should go and—at least on this particular score —I have not departed from it. I have had friends like Percy Cavill who sometimes hit the bottle and I regard this as their own affair. But it is rarely fun for a sober man to be crowded in with a bunch of drunks, even if he is well. Being desperately seasick doesn't help matters. It was with great relief that I finally stepped ashore at Long Cay and looked up Commissioner Pyfrom.

The commissioner was a café-au-lait-colored, very roly-poly gentleman with a quick smile. He was frankly both pleased and surprised to see me. I had written him I was coming. "But a great many persons write," he told me. "I am kept fairly busy answering letters. You are the first one ever actually to show up."

But since I was there he began immediately to tell me about his district, speaking of it with an affection that was contagious. He talked about the agricultural problems: the perfect weather but the lack of fertilizers, the lack of markets. He talked about the welfare of the people: there were not enough employment opportunities; because of this and because of poor communications between the islands there were acute dietary problems. Doctors were almost unknown. Yet despite this, the people themselves were wonderful.

I learned a great deal in a very short time from Commissioner Pyfrom. Then he apologized for talking so much, saying he knew I wanted to rest, and called in his constable, a Mr. Whylly. Mr. Whylly, who insisted on carrying my gunnysack

27

handbag, led me to a lovely little cottage almost buried among bougainvillaea and hibiscus bushes. It was for rent—for six shillings a day, including meals.

The meals were furnished by Mrs. Whylly, who proved to be one of the kindest, most pleasant, most dynamic characters I have ever known. She was a large, light-skinned colored woman with an almost passionate love for hard work. She had horses, sheep, goats, hogs, and poultry; she raised her own corn and other crops in fields scattered all over the island and rushed furiously from one to the other, in between times rushing back to her own home, next door to the guest house, to prepare my meals, which she served on trays. She then stood by with a brush, to keep off the flies while I dined. She had hollowed out a large mortar in the stump of a tree and in this she ground her own meal, using a pestle that looked something like an overgrown baseball bat. The meal was winnowed by placing the dehulled grains in a shallow basket, then holding the basket aloft and shaking it in a spot where the trade winds blew steadily. Watching her at this, I was reminded of the words of the Psalmist, "The ungodly are not so, but are like the chaff which the wind driveth away." Mrs. Whylly was definitely not of the ungodly.

I had told Commissioner Pyfrom that because of my limited time I could remain on Long Cay only until the mailboat returned on its way back to Nassau, two days later. But while I was eating my first supper under the protecting fan of Mrs. Whylly the commissioner arrived. He had an idea. "Next week," he told me, "I am to take a trip to Acklins, and the week after that to Crooked Island. If you could stay over until the second mailboat, which will be another two weeks, I'd love to have you go with me."

It took me only a moment to decide. It would mean giving up my Abaco trip for that summer; but it would mean visiting two of the most out-of-the-way Bahama islands, islands I would have difficulty in visiting any other way. I told Mr. Pyfrom he had a passenger.

We went in Mr. Pyfrom's *Sonny Boy,* a comfortable, twenty-

28

one-foot sailboat with a crew of two: Captain Rose and a tall, well-built youngster named Nigel. Captain Rose was a wizened, very black little man. He had been in a railroad accident in the United States and had lost both legs about halfway between the ankles and knees. On land he rode about on a donkey. On the *Sonny Boy* he crawled, but he crawled with a speed that was absolutely incredible. He got around far faster than I could —and certainly faster than Nigel. Nigel meant well; he smiled gently and tried to please. He had been raised around boats and appeared to know what he was supposed to do. But he had a tremendous gift for doing it wrong. Both the commissioner and Captain Rose spent most of their time shouting at Nigel.

We set sail on a Monday evening and with daylight were approaching Acklins. This is a very long, very narrow island with a population, Mr. Pyfrom told me, of about 1800 living in a dozen or so tiny settlements. As we approached in the early morning the only person visible was a man sculling a dinghy near the shore. Mr. Pyfrom hailed him and learned he had been gathering seabird eggs. The commissioner immediately asked to buy some. They were almost as large as hen eggs, the shells conspicuously speckled with brown.

Mr. Pyfrom passed them to Nigel with careful instructions on how to cook them for breakfast. But when we sat down to eat I was sure Nigel had done it again. The yolks of the eggs were bright pink! However, neither the commissioner nor Captain Rose seemed startled. And the eggs were delicious.

Shortly after breakfast, still sailing along the Acklins coastline, Mr. Pyfrom spied another dinghy and hailed it. This man had a freshly killed goat, and the commissioner entered into protracted negotiations to buy some of it. When finally the deal was closed and the goat meat aboard, Mr. Pyfrom seemed unreasonably delighted. But he explained that there are no corner butcher shops in the out-islands and practically no refrigeration. The acquisition of any kind of meat is a real achievement.

Our first stop on Acklins was at the settlement of Pompey Bay. Here the water was so shallow the *Sonny Boy* had to anchor almost a mile from shore. We poled in with the dinghy.

29

On the beach the commissioner was met by several men who had been waiting for him, and as he had some official business he asked if I wished to visit the school while I waited.

I found it without difficulty. The door was in the back and I went around to it. I was hardly dressed for a formal visit— barefooted, with torn shorts wet from the dinghy ride, an old sports shirt; but I thought that possibly I could slip in quietly and sit down and watch.

I stepped up to the doorway. The children had their backs to me but the teacher was facing me. The instant I appeared in the door he leaped to his feet. "So this is Mr. Cottman!" he boomed in a voice that must have been heard over a good part of Acklins. "We have been looking for you all morning. Come in, sir! We have prepared a place of honor for you." He came striding down the room toward me, his hand outstretched. The children all stood up and turned, staring at me. Many of them, I learned later, had never before seen a white man.

But if they were surprised, so was I. And to this day I don't know how the teacher got his information about me.

Yet they had indeed prepared a place of honor for me. On the teacher's platform there was a large chair with a cushion on the seat and another on the back. When I was enthroned here the teacher turned back to the class. "This," he said in a tone that might have been used to introduce King George, "is Mr. Cottman. Mr. Cottman represents for us the teaching profession of America!"

He paused. I looked down at my bare feet and ragged shorts and blushed. I have always believed that American teachers are underpaid, but this seemed to be overdoing it.

"Now, Mr. Cottman," the teacher continued, "we have prepared a program for you. Would you like for us to sing?"

I assured him I would. He turned to the class. "We will sing 'Old Black Joe,' " he boomed. I was a bit startled at the choice but later found it was an out-island favorite. The teacher tilted back his head and opened his mouth. The sound that came out was so strangely different from anything that had preceded it

30

I almost jumped from my throne. It was a thin, high falsetto. "Do-o-oh."

The children answered in the same pitch. "Do-o-oh."

Still in the same falsetto the teacher sang, keeping time with a stick, "Gone are the days—" He waved the stick violently, shouted, "Now! One! Two!" The children took it from there and carried it to the end, with zest.

Several other songs followed, then "pieces" were called for. Each child when he came forward would bow to me, "Mr. Gentleman." Then to the teacher, "Mr. Sawyer." Then to the pupils, "Classmates." This last in a British accent as broad as that of Captain Rees. But they spoke their pieces very well indeed. I was particularly impressed with one mulatto youngster about thirteen who recited Kipling's "Recessional." It was elocution of the old school, but it contained real feeling.

With the pieces over I was asked to say a few words. Since I had been introduced as a representative of the teaching profession in America, I tried to tell them something about American schools. It was quickly obvious I wasn't getting over. The faces were polite, but they seemed more interested in the shape and color of my bare feet than in what I was saying. So I told them a little of my experiences since coming to the Bahamas: my difficulty in eating a mango, and my reaction to the mate of the *Clipper K*'s order to "Watch the boom." This was speaking their language and they roared with laughter.

When it was time to meet Mr. Pyfrom the teacher appointed a youngster named Cyril Tynes to go with me. This was the boy who had recited the "Recessional" and I complimented him on it. He told me he loved to read but had no books of his own. "When I get home," I told him, "I'll send you some books."

He looked up at me with delight and doubt both showing in his face. "A book?" he said. "You will send me a book?"

I promised him I would.

The doubt still showed. But all the way down the street he kept repeating, "That would be wonderful. I would thank you, sir."

31

That evening the commissioner called an outdoor meeting of the people. Perhaps Cyril had spread the word about my promise, for in discussing the troubles of the settlement several persons mentioned there was no library of any kind. The government had promised a small library but it had not been forthcoming. After an impassioned speech on this subject by Mr. Sawyer, the schoolteacher, I was asked to say a few words. So I not only repeated my promise to send Cyril a book of his own, I promised to send enough books to serve as the nucleus of a small library. I was cheered, loud and lustily.

Early next morning Cyril appeared at the house where Mr. Pyfrom and I had spent the night. He wanted to see me. When I went to the door he said, "I have brought you a little present. So you won't forget me."

It was a beautiful pink conch pearl. I had never before seen one, or even heard of them. Cyril told me they sometimes developed inside conchs, just as the usual pearl develops in an oyster. When perfect they are of considerable value. This one had a flaw that kept it from being commercial. But it was still lovely, and it was his proudest possession.

If there had been any chance of my forgetting my promise about the books, that did away with it.

Our next port was the settlement of Spring Point where the commissioner was to hold court. This was done in a long, one-room government building. There were benches for the audience, a box for the accused to stand in, another for the witness, and a raised platform with a table and chair for the commissioner. There were no lawyers.

The first case was that of one very black woman who had called another some very black names. Asked what these were, the plaintiff entered into a spirited recital that held the crowd spellbound until someone interrupted, calling the commissioner's attention to the presence of a very young child. Court was suspended and the child removed. Once more the plaintiff began her recital, and it was quite a recital indeed.

The witness in the case was the constable, an ugly little man with very short legs and a huge nose. He duly swore he had heard the defendant call the plaintiff— The commissioner stopped him. "There is no need to repeat the words, Mr. Edwards. We have heard enough to establish the point."

"Yessir, but she sure called her that and—"

The defendant could take no more. She leaped to her feet and, stabbing a long arm toward the constable, shouted, "You know why he testify against me? Because he try to make love to me and he such a ugly little runt I want nuthin' to do with him and now he vex with me!"

The courtroom burst into laughter. The constable glared and the commissioner banged with the gavel. When order was restored he addressed the defendant. "You may have been provoked. I have no doubt you were. But you did say these bad things, so I am going to fine you ten shillings."

The woman looked in her purse. "Mr. Pyfrom, I only got seven and sixpence."

"Well," the commissioner said, "you have friends here. They have made that obvious. So borrow the other two and six or I'll have to put you in jail."

The woman scurried through the crowd. In a few moments she was back in front of the commissioner. "Here de ten shilling, Mr. Pyfrom."

The next case had, apparently, begun several years before when a horse belonging to one man got into a fight with another man's horse and injured it. The owner of the injured horse sued for one pound damages. However, the case had been postponed a number of times because of the failure of witnesses to appear. Both horses were now dead but the suit lingered on and this time Mr. Pyfrom had made a special effort to have all the witnesses present. He heard the testimony and handed down a decision that the plaintiff was due damages but that a pound was too much. Instead he set the compensation at seven and sixpence—about $1.50 at that time. The plaintiff immediately arose to say he was not satisfied and wanted to appeal. Mr. Pyfrom sighed. (The last I heard of this case, several years later, it was still unsettled.)

The last case was that of a man and wife who wanted a

divorce. The commissioner glared sternly at them. "So you want a divorce, and simply because you don't get along so well any more. You ought to be ashamed." Then to each in turn, "Look at her; she is your wife. Look at him; he is your husband."

The two exchanged furtive glances. "Now," said the commissioner, "take hold of hands."

They hesitated. Down came Mr. Pyfrom's gavel with a bang. "Do as I say!" he thundered. "Or I'll put you both in jail!"

They complied, instantly. The lady suppressed an embarrassed giggle. The man ducked his head and grinned sheepishly. "Now," the commissioner said, "offer your wife your arm." And to the wife, "Take his arm!"

Arm in arm they stood there, the lady's giggles more audible. In turn the commissioner's voice was softer. "Now don't come to me again for a divorce because of some unimportant difference. Instead, I want the two of you to walk out of this courtroom arm in arm, and continue right on down the road to your home. And I want you to make love to her, just like you used to do before you were married. And I want you," he said to the woman, "to return his love the way you used to do. Now go."

The courtroom burst into applause. The pair, both of them giggling happily, walked arm in arm down the aisle. Our last glimpse of them, they were far down the road, hurrying now with their arms around one another. I like to believe that the reconciliation was permanent.

After our return to Long Cay Mr. Pyfrom became ill. He delegated his business on Crooked Island to Mr. Whylly, his constable, and I went along with him.

We approached the island from the south and my first view of it was of a high bluff that fell sharply to a broad expanse of mangroves which extended along the water line as far as the eye could see. As we came closer I saw a gap in the mangroves. This was a long, tortuous creek which as we moved into it became narrower and narrower, twisting between walls of mangroves. The wind was against us and we had to tack often, the high bluffs coming closer and closer. Then we rounded a curve and there, pointing straight at us, was a great iron cannon. It was supposed to be, Mr. Whylly told me, a relic of days when pirates sailed the Spanish Main. Many pirates were supposed to have used Crooked Island and there were legends of buried treasure having been discovered now and again. But just what pirate had emplaced this huge cannon, or why or when, nobody knew. Yet there it was, the great dark muzzle pointing straight into any ship that rounded the curve.

Perhaps it was the sight of the cannon. Perhaps it had started even earlier, with my first sight of Crooked Island. Even now, trying very hard to be completely honest with myself, I cannot be sure. But I know that as the *Sonny Boy* moved slowly up that creek something was happening to me. I could feel a tightening of the muscles in my chest and throat, a thickening of the blood in my veins for which there was no logical explanation. Neither Nassau nor Andros, nor even Long Cay or Acklins had affected me in quite this way.

Eventually the creek became too narrow for the *Sonny Boy* to maneuver and we transferred to the dinghy. After another mile we came to what Mr. Whylly referred to as Blacksmith's Landing, a stretch of beach with great bluffs rising on both sides. On the crest of one of these stood the skeleton of what had once been a huge plantation house. It was, Mr. Whylly said, left from the days when slave-owning Loyalists had fled here from the American Revolution and planted vast fields of cotton. But the abolition of slavery had made the cotton fields unprofitable. The owners had moved away, leaving the slaves and, scattered about the island, the decaying ruins of half a dozen mansions.

From the landing a footpath led inland, and after a forty-minute walk we arrived at the settlement of Colonel Hill. It was a pretty little town on a high hilltop. Beyond it a plain, green with vegetation, sloped down to a concave beach which was guarded on each side by the high bluffs that make this island so distinctive. Here Mr. Whylly introduced me to John

Deleveaux who was the local constable, postmaster, and civic leader.

Again I was asked if I wished to visit the school and this time I arrived in the midst of an examination. It was on scouting. (For some reason I have never learned, on Crooked Island scouting was as basic a part of the curriculum for boys as reading.) The questions were written on the blackboard and I still remember a couple of them. "What is the sign for 'I have gone home'?" and "Who is the Patron Saint of Ireland?" I was puzzling over just what this had to do with scouting—I was fairly sure St. Patrick hadn't founded the Boy Scouts—when suddenly the teacher shouted, "Why aren't you writing?" and pointed his finger at a boy sitting motionless at his desk.

"I—I forgot my pencil, sir."

"And you a Boy Scout!" the teacher cried. "The Scout motto is 'Be Prepared!' But you have come to this class unprepared!" Not so the teacher. He had been pacing the aisle with a large bundle of switches in his hand and now he brought the whole bundle down on the boy's back. "You have violated your Scout motto!" he shouted. "For the rest of the day you will sit on the side of the room with the girls!" That, I thought, will teach him to be prepared.

Leaving the school, I walked with Mr. John Deleveaux toward his home where I was to stay until Mr. Whylly finished his work. The sun was blistering hot and I paused under the shade of a tree. The instant I entered the shade it was like entering an air-conditioned room. I became more aware of the breeze and the air had a cool crisp freshness that seemed to have no relation to the air a few feet away in the sunshine. "It is always like that on Crooked Island," Mr. Deleveaux said. "On the hottest kind of day we can be cool in the shade."

I asked what kind of tree we were under and he told me it was a fig. I had never seen a fig tree before. "Do you eat them?" I asked.

"Oh no," he said. "The Bible says, 'Jesus cursed the fig tree.' So nobody would eat them."

He was completely serious about this, and I made no comment. But as I would learn later that same evening, Crooked Island has a number of rather odd religious practices. I was chatting with the Deleveauxs in their home when gradually I became aware of a clamor and shouting that got louder and louder. "It's a meeting," Mr. Deleveaux told me. "A seeking meeting."

Whatever they were seeking, they weren't going to slip up on it with that much noise. I asked what they were looking for.

"They are seeking Jesus," Mr. Deleveaux said. "Would you like to go?"

We went. From the racket I had thought the meeting must be just outside the house. Actually it was in a small church several blocks away and as we stepped through the door the noise became absolutely deafening. Up front on a platform a priest in a black suit was frantically pounding a big bass drum. Nearby a deacon, also in black, his collar wilted with sweat, was waving his arms, exhorting the congregation and mopping his brow with a handkerchief long since soaking wet. In the front row an old woman kept time with the drum by hammering on a frying pan with a huge iron spoon. The congregation, their eyes fixed trancelike on the deacon, were jumping in rhythm with the pounding. It was a strange kind of rigid, mechanical jumping that went on at the same time the people screamed and shrieked. Now and then someone would be seized by a kind of fit and fall thrashing about on the floor.

It was all strangely moving and a little terrifying, and probably very similar to the camp meetings on the American frontier during the great religious revival of the early 1800's. I soon had enough and John Deleveaux and I walked back to his home. The house had only one bedroom, in which there were two beds, one for Mr. and Mrs. Deleveaux and one for their twelve-year-old son. It was now about 10 o'clock; Mr. Whylly had said he would come for me at midnight in order to catch the outgoing tide. I told the Deleveauxs I would wait for him in the parlor.

They simply would not have it. I was their guest and must have the best the house could afford. The bedroom was to be

37

mine and mine alone. Eventually, convinced of the futility of further argument and afraid of hurting their feelings, I accepted. The three of them stretched out on the parlor floor. In the bedroom my guilty conscience and I shared the two beds.

Promptly at midnight Mr. Whylly knocked on the door. The Deleveauxs and I arose from our respective couches and said good-by. I stepped out the door—and into a new and enchanted world.

The moon had risen. It was just past the full, huge and yellow and slightly bent. It gave a light that was like silver rain. Against the moon-touched sky the palm trees seemed etched in ebony. Not a frond stirred. At first there was no sound except for the soft whisper of our feet on the bare earth. Then we were outside the village. Now and then a crab would scurry across the path, a night heron would pass, crying hoarsely.

I had been fascinated with the island in the daytime. Now I was spellbound. I walked slowly. It seemed to me I could feel the moonlight like warm water pouring over me, soaking into me, moving with the blood through my veins. I listened for every night sound, for the cry of every bird as if it were music.

And as we approached the landing I became aware of a new sound. It was a vast, dull humming and I thought at first it was the beginning of a wind in the mangroves. Then we reached the creek; I stepped into the dinghy, and into an almost solid mass of mosquitoes. They not only covered my face and arms and legs; they piled up on me three deep. With one slap I could kill fifty, a hundred, three hundred. I never counted. I couldn't count. They got in my eyes and up my nose. When I started to complain they flew into my mouth. I bit down on a wad of them. Apparently all the mosquitoes in the Bahamas had called a convention to be held that night at Blacksmith's Landing, the main feature to be a feast provided by one bare-legged newcomer to the islands.

Even so, there were enough left over to feed on Mr. Whylly also and he sculled that dinghy like a man possessed. We made it back to the *Sonny Boy* and leaped aboard. The mosquitoes

38

went with us. They made a thick cloud around the boat. When the sail went up it hung limp in the dead air.

And then that miracle of the Bahamas happened as it had the night with Percy Cavill's sand flies. The trade wind came back, steady and fresh. The *Sonny Boy* slid quickly down the creek and into the bay and the mosquitoes vanished. The moon rode high now and every wave in the bay glittered with diamonds.

I wiped the dead mosquitoes out of my eyes and off my face and arms. I looked back at the high bluffs of Crooked Island, silver and black in the moonlight. And I knew that, mosquitoes or not, I was coming back to Crooked Island. I was going to search here for the site of my future home, for the occupation, whatever it might be, of my future life.

5

One Summer Fiasco

WITH the end of the summer I went back to Madison, to teaching science, to a long, cold winter—and to writing letters to Mr. Percy Cavill. I managed to transmit to him some of my enthusiasm for Crooked Island. His sailboat had a small auxiliary motor with one part missing. I sent him the part and we agreed that next summer the two of us would go in his boat from Andros to Crooked Island. If we found a place we both liked, I would buy it and he would stay there and look after it when I had to return to Madison.

These best-laid plans started to go awry almost immediately. Before Christmas Cavill wrote that in trying to build an extra room on his house he had wrestled with a heavy post and ruptured himself. He was afraid he would not be able to make the Crooked Island trip. But in the spring he wrote he was feeling much better and would meet me in Nassau.

So with the first of June I headed happily south. And in a Cincinnati restaurant I ate something that gave me ptomaine poisoning. As a result I spent some extremely miserable hours on the bus and finally a couple of days in a Miami hotel. My stomach was still sore when I took off for Nassau.

Cavill met me, and though I didn't feel very well myself, I was shocked to see the change in him. He was gaunt. The huge frame was still there but his flesh was sunken. His eyes were deep in his face. But he still had his sense of humor. We sat on a park bench in Rawson Square and he told me, making a joke of it, what had happened.

Several weeks before, he had been awakened by a rustling sound in the leaves of his thatched roof. Looking up, he saw by the moonlight, which (like the rain on other occasions) entered his house far too freely, a gigantic chicken snake glide through the fronds. The Bahama chicken snake is not poisonous, but it is incredibly strong. This one was after an egret Cavill had tamed and which slept on one of his rafters. Before Cavill could intercept, the snake grabbed the bird and threw a coil of its body around it.

At almost the same time Cavill grabbed the snake with his left hand, just back of its head. Immediately it released the bird, but not before it had crushed it. In his turn, Cavill set out to choke the snake; and the snake, unable to escape, wrapped itself around his waist and tried to crush him as it had the egret. In the following battle Cavill stumbled and fell. The fall and the terrific pressure of the snake tore open his old rupture. Even so, he was not going to let the snake escape. Still holding it, he rolled into a corner, found the saw with which he had once made my bed, and sawed off the snake's head. Then he passed out.

When he regained consciousness it was daylight but he was too weak and sick to move. He lay there all day and the next night without food or water. Next day he managed to crawl outside and hail some men who were fishing in a dinghy near his house. They had come ashore, given him food and water. One of the men had stayed with him for several days until, with the aid of a homemade truss, he was able to move about.

Now, he told me, he was feeling much better, but still uncertain whether he could make the long trip to Crooked Island. However, he wanted me to come to Andros with him. He had also invited a Nassau druggist, a Mr. Cyril Lightbourn. Cavill wanted to take us on a hunting trip into the little-known interior of Andros. He had arranged passage for the three of us on the *Blacket*, a government sponge boat scheduled to leave the next evening.

I stayed that night at Miss Taylor's rooming house. Mr. Forsyth was there and several other persons I had met the previous summer. But this time it was not a happy visit. This was June 1940. The German armies were sweeping through France and the Low Countries. The radio told only of Allied defeats, one after another.

Early next morning I heard a woman weeping hysterically in the backyard beneath my window. Then I heard Mr. Forsyth's voice speaking to one of the house guests, "Don't do that! This is no time for weeping. We must fight!"

I went downstairs and found Miss Taylor red-eyed. "France has surrendered," she said. "England is fighting on, alone."

She served breakfast, but no one ate much. The radio went on and on with its story of disaster.

I don't think Miss Taylor had ever been in England, but the British Empire had no more loyal citizen. She was a lady of the old school, of Victorian graciousness and courtesy. Her ancestors had been relatives of President Zachary Taylor but loyal to Britain and had left the Colonies after the Revolution. Now, after listening to the radio for about an hour, she leaped to her feet. "I'm going to telephone them," she said, and went out.

A few minutes later she was back. And a few minutes after that the announcer suddenly stopped his catalogue of disaster to say, "One of our esteemed Daughters of the Empire has re-

41

quested that we answer this morning's news by playing 'There'll Always Be an England.'"

Then the music came on and suddenly everyone in the room was standing up, crying but erect. There was a change in the atmosphere that was almost electric. I have an idea that all over Nassau it was the same. That afternoon when I went out for supplies to take to Andros I heard at least a dozen persons still singing, "There'll Always Be an England."

About dark I met Cavill and Mr. Lightbourn and we went aboard the *Blacket*. The trip was smooth and I slept soundly until next morning when I awoke to find Cavill leaning over me, grinning. "I've got something to show you," he said, and held up a flying fish.

I asked how he had caught it. "Oh," he said, "I don't sleep well, so I was on deck about 4 this morning and saw a school of them fly out from under the bow. I thought that as a science teacher you might be interested in them; so I jumped overboard and caught this one. Then I grabbed the dinghy we are towing as it passed, and climbed back aboard."

My first startled thought was of what would have happened if he had missed the dinghy. "Why," he said casually, "I'd have swum ashore. It was only four or five miles."

And he could have, sixty-four years old, rupture and all. On the other hand, catching a flying fish bare-handed at night in the open sea is, admittedly, something else. But I had seen Percy Cavill swim and I believed him.

The *Blacket* stopped off Cavill's place about 10 A.M., and we were rowed ashore. I had brought a box of food, as had Mr. Lightbourn. "I say," he remarked as we were carrying them up the hill to Cavill's house, "my supplies seem to be leaking."

Mine were also, so we put them down to examine. I had brought lard, among other things, and the lard had been wrapped in paper and put near the top of the box. On the *Blacket*, the box, apparently, had been put near the engine. The lard had melted and soaked down into the bread, cake, cheese, and everything else into which it possibly could soak. Lightbourn's box was in even worse shape. Someone had sat on it, crushing both a dozen eggs and a dozen very ripe bananas. The result was a kind of banana pudding thoroughly mixed with uncooked scrambled eggs, and this had become homogenized with everything else in his box.

There was, as Cavill remarked, no benefit in crying over spilled bananas, so we picked up the boxes and carried them on to the house. This was almost exactly as I had seen it last: the unwashed dishes, the smoky lamp, the tin contraption on the floor in which Cavill built his smudge fires, the wild litter of odds and ends. The hen's nest was still under the bed. The extra room which he had started last fall was still incomplete; but nailed to the door was the skin of the chicken snake with which he had done battle. Even with the head and part of the body missing it was over six feet long.

Since his snake episode, Cavill had employed a man named Ed to stay with him, and that afternoon the four of us went fishing. Somebody sighted—or claimed to sight—a school of fish, and all of us jumped overboard into water about three feet deep. Cavill and Lightbourn took the two ends of a long net and started walking in the same direction, about a hundred feet apart, the net trailing behind them in a great semicircle. Ed and I were sent ahead, some distance apart, and told to drive the fish into the net. Suddenly Cavill began to shout, "They're coming toward you, Evans! Head 'em off!" I looked in vain for the fish. "That way!" he shouted, pointing. "Run! Don't let 'em get around you!" I began to run. "Faster!" Cavill shouted.

I was running as fast as a man can run in three feet of water. But Cavill, Lightbourn, and Ed were all screaming for greater effort and all pointing in different directions. Finally I stopped, exhausted.

"You let them get away," Cavill yelled.

"If you had given it a bit more effort," Lightbourn said, "you'd have headed them."

43

"You run de wrong way," Ed said.

"The wrong way? You were all pointing in different directions. What did you expect me to do, go straight up?"

But they were all laughing now. And finally it dawned on me that this was a Bahamian version of the ancient game of snipe hunting. Even so, when the net was pulled in we had at least caught one very small barracuda.

It was after dark when we got back to the house. Cavill lighted the lamp, then cleaned and salted the barracuda. Meanwhile Lightbourn and I tried to salvage something to eat from our food boxes. I'm not sure what success he had; but the ants had found their way into my box in great numbers. They had become as hopelessly entangled in the already rancid lard as the lard was with the rest of the food. But I found a tin of evaporated milk and, using some of the straw from my bed, wiped it partially clean. On the floor under the table I found a hammer and nail and punched a hole in the can. Then from the bottom of the box I fished out a slab of cheese. Using Cavill's pocket knife, I scraped off as much of the lard and dead ants as possible.

About this time my stomach, still weak from the ptomaine, rebelled.

When I was able I got out pen and paper to write a letter home. I began describing the room as I saw it by the dim light of the smoky lamp. Mr. Lightbourn was trying vainly to make himself comfortable in a kind of homemade posture chair which Cavill had given him to sleep in. The wind had stopped; the sand flies and the smoke from Cavill's smudge came in alternating waves. Ed sat on some piece of junk, his back against the wall, apparently immune to everything. I sat at the rickety table, leaning into the heat of the lamp in an effort to see. With my left hand I would wipe the stinging smoke from my eyes, then a moment later battle with the sand flies.

And all at once it occurred to me that in a strange way I was taking pleasure in my own discomfort, and in describing it for my family back home. I remembered my aunt saying to me about a letter I had written the previous summer, "You are

44

proud of yourself, aren't you? You are proud that you could put up with those things. It stuck out in every line you wrote." At the time I had denied it. But now, trying to be honest with myself, I realized there was a great deal of truth in what she had said. I had always had a fancy for colorful living; yet all my life I had lived quietly under the same roof with my family. I had been a quiet child; I had got into the very minimum of fights. I had been a quiet young man, drably teaching school in the daytime and coming home to my father and mother and aunt at night. I had loved them. I did love them. But now it occurred to me this was a kind of rebellion. I was trying to prove to myself and to them that when necessary I could be as tough as anyone else.

With that settled in my mind I went ahead to finish the letter, telling them of our planned hunting trip into the interior of Andros and of how, after that, I was looking forward to my return to Crooked Island.

But, as I have indicated, this was one of those summers.

Cavill had repaired the motor for which I had sent him the part, but it was still in the middle of the cottage floor. Next morning he decided to put it in the boat. Being the kind of man he was, he said nothing to anybody but bent over and picked up the motor. It weighed 200 pounds. He took three steps and fell face down in a dead faint.

Lightbourn and I picked him up and put him on his bed. Then we looked at one another helplessly. But in a few moments Cavill opened his eyes. "Sorry," he said, his voice barely audible. "We're going to have to cancel the hunting trip."

We told him to be quiet and rest. Instead he struggled to sit up. "I'm a sick old man," he said in disgust. "You two had best get to Mangrove Cay and find a chance back to Nassau."

We tried to persuade him to go to Nassau with us and to the hospital. It was useless. "Ed is with me," he said. "He'll take good care of me. I'll be around again soon, and I'll meet you in Nassau later this summer."

He got off the bed and began to move slowly about the

45

house. But it was forced motion. He was even stacking dishes and making a pretense of cleaning up. He was chatting, joking as usual; but it was obviously done with strain. It was apparent that he wanted to be alone, like a sick animal, and was not going to rest until he was. So Lightbourn and I gathered the few things we had brought and prepared for the trip to Mangrove Cay.

There were two boats available, Ed's and Cavill's. Cavill told Ed to get both ready: he was going to accompany us part of the way. I believe now that he was anxious for us to leave, yet at the same time dreaded to see us go. In one way he wanted to postpone the parting as long as possible.

About 4 P.M. we were ready. At the door I turned and looked back into that strange, topsy-turvy room: Lightbourn's reclining chair, Cavill's unmade bed with the hen's nest beneath it, the motor in the middle of the floor, the sand-fly smoker, the odds and ends of tools and junk, and on the table the smoky lamp. Beside it was one lone plate holding the tiny, salted barracuda. This would be Cavill's supper, which he would cook when he returned home. From it a line of ants moved back and forth across the table.

I closed the door and followed the others down the hill to the waiting boats.

Cavill's boat had a sail, but Ed's did not. Lightbourn and I got in the boat with Cavill and we towed the other holding Ed and the luggage. There was almost no conversation. Off the point of the cay Cavill lowered his sail and Ed came alongside. Lightbourn and I got into his boat.

"Sorry I can't get to Crooked Island with you," Cavill said. "But I'll meet you in Nassau later in the summer."

"Sure," I said. "I'll let you know when I'll be back there."

He hoisted his sail. The boat swung away. He waved, a single gesture of his arm, then did not look toward us again.

With Ed alternately sculling and poling we reached Mangrove Cay before dark. There we found a sloop about to leave for Nassau. It was a filthy little boat alive with cockroaches. The cabin stank and I began to get seasick. I went on deck.

The sea was choppy; the spray came in sheets. But that was better than the cabin, so I spent the night on deck.

With daylight we ran into a dead calm. The sail hung limp against the mast and the sun was broiling. The cabin was an oven and the deck was a frying pan. Finally, about dark, a wind came up and by midnight we reached Nassau.

In Nassau the talk was of Dunkirk and of the coming invasion of Britain. Nobody smiled. And nobody, it seemed, was going toward Crooked Island. I had missed the mailboat and would have to wait two weeks for the next one. So I waited. And the day before it was to sail I got a cable from my aunt. My mother was seriously ill and I was wanted at home.

I canceled my passage on the mailboat and went back to Indiana.

6

Fools Rush In

In November I had a letter from Mr. Lightbourn in Nassau. Percy Cavill had died. When I added up the hours I had spent with him I was amazed to realize they totaled no more than a week. Yet to me he had been a kind of symbol. I knew I could never enjoy living in an environment quite as chaotic as Cavill's; yet he had represented some of the romance and adventure I dreamed about. But far more than that—he had been a friend.

Two months later I was greatly saddened by the loss of my mother. During the previous summer she had broken her hip and had been confined to her bed ever since. My father too had been in failing health for several years and he also was in bed most of the time. His death followed my mother's by only four months. I had been devoted to both my parents, and for me that winter and spring of 1940–41 was the worst I have ever experienced, both physically and emotionally. When school let out in the spring I had little mind for a vacation in the Bahamas. But my aunt insisted I needed a change and should go.

I was easy to persuade. My parents had been my one real tie to Madison and to my job as a schoolteacher. Now they were gone, and more and more I began to dream of actually buying land on one of the out-islands and living there. Just what kind of a life I would lead there, I did not know. But I felt that whatever kind it was, it would not slip through my fingers without me ever really feeling it, enjoying it, as life seemed to do in Madison. In Madison I was a schoolteacher, one among many. On some remote out-island perhaps I could be somebody, unique, a personage. I felt sure that I could somehow find a way of earning a living, yet being my own boss. Perhaps I might even do something of value. I didn't know what. I just dreamed. One of my dreams was of setting up a little laboratory and doing experimental work on cold light. My Master's thesis had been written on the spectral distribution of chemiluminescence and I had continued to do some work along this line.

Consequently, as my spirits revived I became anxious to return to the Bahamas. And this time an old friend, the Reverend Robert Andry, who had been intrigued by my stories of the islands, wanted to go with me. Early in June we flew down.

We settled at Miss Taylor's and made a tour of the local docks trying to find some way to Long Cay. The mailboat had just left and no small boats were in from those parts. Mr. Whylly had written me that his sailboat, the *Lady May,* would be in Nassau about this time and could take us to Long Cay. But day after day passed and there was no sign of it. I tried to telegraph Whylly, but the Long Cay wireless station was broken down.

48

I remembered Percy Cavill telling me that if I had not arrived at Mangrove Cay on June 4 he would have waited, because "Time doesn't mean much out here." Perhaps I was getting acclimated; also, I had all summer. But Bob had only six weeks' vacation. His time was running out and he was in a great hurry to get going. So it was with vast excitement he came rushing into Miss Taylor's one day with the news he had found a boat. She was a twenty-foot sloop named the *Cheerful*, just arrived from Acklins and due to leave for Long Cay the following Saturday.

Fools rush in, they say, where angels and wise men fear to tread. It is also said that the moment a woman's baby is born she forgets the pain connected with the labor. Seasickness and I have a somewhat similar connection. No matter how seasick I may have been, when I get on dry land, feeling fine, and look out at a boat I think: Wouldn't it be wonderful to be out there sailing! So instead of taking one quick look at the *Cheerful* and going straight back to Miss Taylor's comfortable, landbased house, I was almost as thrilled as Bob at the idea of making such a long trip in such a cute little boat with such an optimistic name.

We bought provisions. In our blissful ignorance we bought such things as bread, eggs (and after I had seen Mr. Lightbourn's eggs too), and very ripe fruit. Early Saturday morning we arrived with all our gear on the dock, to find a big fortyfoot sloop tied up right alongside the little *Cheerful*. It was the *Lady May*.

And Mrs. Whylly, the captain told us, had carefully cleaned the cabin, put fresh bedding on the bunks, and provided every convenience she could think of. Unfortunately the *Lady May* was not to leave Nassau until the following Thursday.

But Bob's time was short and we were in a hurry. We couldn't wait until Thursday. We explained this to the captain of the *Lady May*, who merely shook his head in wonder. "You leave on the *Cheerful* today," he said. "I leave next Thursday night. But I'll be in Long Cay first."

It sounded like, "You take the high road and I'll take the low road," and we thought he was joking. But as the mystery writers so frequently put it: "Little did we know."

So we went happily aboard the *Cheerful*. There was a tiny cabin just large enough for two bunks, which were assigned to Bob and me. With our luggage it was filled to overflowing. The crew, which consisted of captain, cook, and mate, would take turns sleeping in the freight-filled hold.

The captain was a dark, thin, Acklins Islander named Luther Bain. All Acklins Islanders talk "deep," as they put it, compared to the "shallow" talk of outsiders. But Luther Bain not only spoke this "deep" Acklins Island accent, but spoke it in a bass voice that would have shamed a bullfrog. The first words I heard him say after the sail went up was, "Headwind."

We were trying to go southeast and the wind was blowing northwest. Bob and I were no sailors, but we were soon familiar with the resulting routine. "Good full!" Captain Bain would boom, standing in the bow. The man at the tiller would draw it toward him and the little boat would lean still more on her side. "Let's go back!" Captain Bain would bellow. The helmsman would push the tiller as far as possible from him. The sail would begin to flap; the boom would slowly swing from one side of the boat to the center. There it would hang, apparently undecided. The *Cheerful*, undecided also, would pause. Then the boom would move slowly on to the other side. Everyone would duck. The wind would fill the sail again and we would start moving—if not back to where we had come from, then very close to it.

This went on all day and all night, and all the next day, and the next. Or so I was told. After the first few hours I ceased to notice. I was seasick. Just over the bunks hung the Sunday suits of the captain, cook, and mate, each with a paper bag over it. As the *Cheerful* rolled (and it rolled and rolled) the bags swung incessantly back and forth just over our heads. By the third day this got on Bob's nerves. He said it reminded him of *The Pit and the Pendulum*. At that point I would have been happy to change places with Mr. Poe's hero.

50

It took six days to reach the south end of Long Island. By then our bread was moldy, our fruit rotten, our eggs broken. Bob, who proved a far better sailor than I, was complaining of hunger. But of all the things I didn't want to hear about, food (like Abou Ben Adhem) led all the rest.

All this time we had been sailing over comparatively shallow water. The great ocean swells did not come here. Instead the water was choppy. There was no set rhythm to it and the *Cheerful* simply bucked like an unbroken horse. But on Friday we moved out from behind Long Island into the tremendous ocean depths of the Crooked Island Passage. Here the nature of the waves changed. They no longer slapped at the *Cheerful* but came in long, sleek, tremendous mountains. Up the sides of these the little *Cheerful* rode like a cork, hung suspended on the crest like a feather, and plunged down the far side like a shot duck. My poor stomach, which had been adjusting itself to the choppy water, was caught totally off guard. As the *Cheerful* plunged down the slope of a wave my stomach lurched upward. It passed through my throat into my mouth, where I tried to stop it with clenched teeth and open palm. Then as the *Cheerful* shot up the next wave my stomach shot down.

I was lying on my bunk when I heard Captain Bain boom, "Here come a squall." Looking up through the open hatchway, I observed, with only minor interest, that the sky had gone purple and black. A moment later the wind struck with a wild howling sound. The *Cheerful* seemed to quit riding the waves and simply to be blown or hurled from one to another. Sometimes there were tremendous waves towering over us; sometimes looking over the rail was like looking out of an airplane. About this time the man at the helm shouted, "De main sheet pop!" The words meant nothing to me, but I was soon aware of what had happened. The main line which ran from the helmsman out to the end of the boom and kept the sail in position had broken. The boom swung wildly, viciously, from side to side. In those tremendous rolling seas it seemed impossible to catch it. I looked at Captain Bain and realized, dimly,

51

that he was scared. Bob, sitting beside me, was obviously scared. In fact, everybody was scared. Except me. I just didn't care.

In the Bahamas they say there are two stages of seasickness: first, you are afraid you are going to die; and second, you are afraid that you won't. I had reached the second stage.

By the Grace of God and the heroic efforts of captain and crew the runaway boom was finally captured and tied down. The mainsail was lowered. The jib was left up, the boat was turned, and with the wind behind us we headed back into the shelter of Long Island and a little cove.

I had often read about the joy of sailors on reaching a safe harbor. I suppose that is what the crew of the *Cheerful* felt. They shouted and clapped one another on the back. As for me, I lay on the deck and looked over the side at the calm, glass-clear water and wondered if life were so important a possession after all.

But things improved. Bob had noted two small houses nearby as we came into the cove and he asked the captain to put us ashore to see if we could buy any food. I was not yet interested in food, but I was definitely interested in getting ashore.

The houses were close to where the dinghy dropped us. We knocked on the door of the first one. It opened a crack and a very short, very dark man stared out suspiciously. I think he believed we were German spies. At any rate he refused to sell us any food. But eventually he told us there was a little store about two miles away. Maybe we could get food there.

By now I was beginning to be interested. Since leaving Nassau six days before, my intake had been very little and my output excessive. With every step I became more aware of the need for nourishment.

Both Bob and I had come ashore barefooted. The path we followed was extremely rocky. At times it ceased to be a path altogether. There were huge piles of rock over which we had to climb on hands and knees. By now I was almost too weak to climb. On the other hand, my feet were tougher than Bob's.

53

I had always liked to go barefooted when possible, but this was Bob's first time since he was a boy. The rocks cut his feet. He had to lean on me for support, and I had to cling to him to keep from falling in sheer exhaustion. In this way, the blind leading the blind, we staggered up to the little store just about dusk.

A small, ancient colored lady sat on the front steps. "Do you have any bread?" I asked.

She considered the question for a long moment, then shook her head. "I had some last week. It all gone now."

"How about some bananas?"

Again she pondered the matter. "I had me some last week. But they gone now."

"Any eggs?"

"I had two, but they gone, too."

"What have you got we could eat?"

Again she took mental inventory. "Seem like I'm right out of everything."

A little desperately Bob asked her if she had any water. Her face lit up. "Yessuh. I got water."

So, fortified by a drink of water, we started back for the *Cheerful*. By now it was dark. The path had been hard enough to follow in the daytime and now we kept losing it. The whole way Bob apparently stepped on nothing but razor-edged rocks or cactus. It was 9 o'clock by the time we reached the shore— and saw that because of the outgoing tide the *Cheerful* had moved farther out. The wind blew from it to us, and when we tried to call, our voices blew right back in our faces. We could hear the sounds aboard the *Cheerful,* but they could not hear us.

Eventually Captain Bain became worried by our absence. He sculled ashore and found us. And on board the *Cheerful* we learned the crew had made moonbread and caught fish. Never did a meal taste better.

Next day the captain looked out toward the ocean and shook his head. "We can't make it today. Too much sea."

I asked to be put ashore. The water in the cove was calm,

54

but I still liked the feel of the beach. However, the only shade ashore was from scrub palms and these grew back from the beach among the rocks. I tried making a bed of palm fronds, but these were almost as hard as the rocks. Also, they were slippery. Every time I started to doze I skidded off the bed into the rocks. For food I munched on the piece of moonbread the cook had given me.

The next day was Sunday. Again the captain looked at the ocean and shook his head. By now the cook's moonbread was moldy and he had very little flour left to make more. The rough weather, or something, had disturbed the fish and no more had been caught. Bob and I went ashore and sat under a palm tree. "I have read about men being cast ashore on a desert island," he said. "I never thought it was going to happen to me."

I looked at my watch. It was noon; it would be 11 A.M., back in Madison. I looked at Bob and began to laugh. His blond hair was matted with sweat and salt water. His normally pink complexion did not take to suntan: his nose was as red as a burlesque drunk's and his ears were raw, and most of his face was covered with beard. He wore a dirty T shirt and ragged shorts. His legs were sunburned and his feet were swollen. "Right at this moment," I said, "the congregation of your church is assembling for service. I wish they could get a look at their pastor."

Monday morning was a repetition of Sunday. The captain looked toward the ocean and shook his head. The cook looked at the fish lines and found nothing. Bob and I were about to go ashore when a big sailboat rounded the end of the cove. Captain Bain hailed her and she came alongside. It was the *Lady May*.

The captain was gracious. He took us aboard and fed us with only a brief "I told you so." Then we sailed out of the cove and started across the Crooked Island Passage.

Where the *Cheerful* had turned back the *Lady May* kept going. But the water was just as rough as it ever had been. I promptly lost my breakfast. I tried to lie down and rolled out

55

of the bunk. There was no place to sit down. For fifteen miserable hours I stood, clutching the top of the hatch leading down into the cabin and swaying with the rhythm of the boat.

It was midnight when we reached Long Cay. Mrs. Whylly had heard us coming and had her guest house all ready. There was a hot tub in which to wash off the nine days' accumulation of *Cheerful* dirt. There was a hot meal. Then clean sheets on a bed that stayed perfectly, blessedly motionless.

I lay in the bed and tried to think back over the past nine days. Most of that time I had been just about as miserable as it is possible for a human being to be and still live. By every law of reason I should be anxious to get out of this country and never come back.

But I wasn't. Instead, I had a strange feeling that I had come home, that if I had not yet found what I was searching for, I would before long. I was looking happily forward to the morning.

Or rather, I was for a few minutes. Then I was asleep.

7

Gun Bluff

By the time Bob and I recovered from our *Cheerful* journey his time had almost run out. He had to get the first mailboat back to Nassau and fly from there to Madison. But I had another six weeks and stayed on at Long Cay, looking for a way across to Crooked Island.

Mr. Whylly found it for me. Three Crooked Islanders had come to Long Cay in a sailboat and were returning home. They were Harry McKinney and the Scavella brothers, Frank

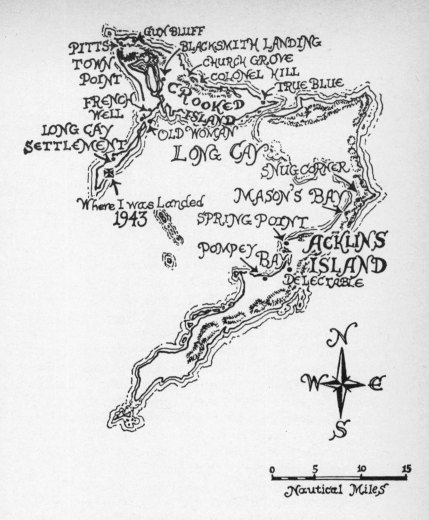

GUN BLUFF
PITTS
TOWN
POINT
BLACKSMITH LANDING
CHURCH GROVE
COLONEL HILL
TRUE BLUE
CROOKED
ISLAND
FRENCH
WELL
OLD WOMAN
LONG CAY
SETTLEMENT
LONG CAY
SNUG CORNER
MASON'S BAY
Where I was Landed
1943
SPRING POINT
POMPEY BAY
ACKLINS
ISLAND
DELECTABLE

N
W E
S

0 5 10 15
Nautical Miles

and Fred. It would have been impossible to find three persons
better suited to take care of the greenhorn traveler and possible settler. Mr. McKinney was the postmaster at Landrail
Point, one of the tiny settlements that dot Crooked Island; he
also had a sister who would rent me a house for twelve shillings
($2.40) a month. Frank Scavella was the lay preacher for the
Seventh Day Adventist Church; but more important from my

57

point of view, he had a store. And Fred Scavella, as I quickly learned after saying I might buy land and build a house, was a builder.

What I was looking for, I told them, was a place with a high hill close to the sea, a sandy beach, a little harbor, a place not too close to the settlement but not too far, and with a road leading from it to the settlement. Also, it had to be for sale, cheap. That was all. I expected them, naturally, to laugh. Instead each one rubbed his chin thoughtfully and gazed ahead toward the island. Finally Mr. McKinney spoke. "It sound like Gun Bluff."

"Why yes," said Fred Scavella, "it do indeed."

We were approaching Crooked Island from the southwest, toward Landrail Point, and from here Gun Bluff was not visible. But it was a bluff, McKinney told me. In the old days it had been the site of a British fortification against the pirates and until the previous year two of the ancient guns were still there. Then they had been destroyed with dynamite and the fragments sent to help in Britain's war effort. There was also an abandoned rock quarry nearby. At the foot of the bluff, on one side, was a beach; on the other there was a small bight in the shore that would serve as anchorage in ordinary weather. All this was four miles from Landrail Point by road, five miles if you walked the beach, and about six miles if you went by sailboat.

It sounded almost too good, and even before I set foot at Landrail Point I was itching to see Gun Bluff.

The house I rented from McKinney's sister was of frame construction although most of the houses on Crooked Island, where timber is very scarce, are made of white limestone. Tiny, half buried among hibiscus and Australian pines, it looked like a doll's house. There were two rooms, very sparsely furnished, but clean. And there was a kitchen. This, like most of those on Crooked Island, was actually a separate little house, a few feet from the other. There was no stove, but a huge open fireplace. And I was to do my own cooking.

Well, I had been a scoutmaster back in Madison. I was supposed to be able to rub two sticks together to make a fire and cook over it outdoors. Maybe I could do it indoors. And though I have always liked good food, I have also taken a certain pride in being able to get along on whatever came my way.

The main thing was to see Gun Bluff, and next morning McKinney and Fred Scavella took me there. We walked the little road which skirted the beach for a short distance, then cut back across the island to strike the beach again on the northeast side. Here McKinney stopped and pointed. "That's Gun Bluff."

It was still two miles away, a small point of land thrusting out against the ocean. From where I stood the bluff seemed to rise perpendicularly, a full seventy feet. Overgrown with low bushes, it was a solid green wall against the sky. At the foot of the wall there was a beach, and beyond that the Atlantic.

As we went closer I could see that the bluff, though steep, didn't go straight up. There was a path through the bushes and we followed it to the top. Then I turned and looked back. On my left the island sloped downward in a long sweep to a point of land three miles away. Off this point, perhaps a half mile at sea, there was another island, a tiny one, topped by the white spire of a lighthouse. It gave depth and perspective to the view. It made you aware that, though invisible, there were other human beings within a few miles. In the other direction, ahead and to the right, there was the Atlantic Ocean and the long coastline of Crooked Island.

It was the place I had been looking for. It was where I wanted to build a home.

There remained the matter of whether or not it was for sale, at a price I could afford. According to a map I had brought from Nassau, the land belonged to a Mr. H. A. McKinney (no relation of my friend the postmaster) who lived in Nassau. I immediately wrote to him, then settled down restlessly to await an answer.

About this time Cyril Tynes, the boy I had heard recite the "Recessional" two years before on Acklins, heard I was in the

59

islands and came over to thank me for the books I had sent to him and to the village library. He stayed on a few weeks. As Percy Cavill had said, time doesn't mean much in the Bahamas. Besides, I was glad to have him. He was obviously a smart youngster, curious and anxious to learn. I began to tutor him in basic science.

It was Cyril who informed me that the local Pentecostal church, known to the other denominations as Jumpers, could not have night meetings any more because the preacher had broken his lantern and was so old he could no longer find his way home in the dark. However, a visiting preacher came from Long Cay and held a night meeting to which Cyril and I went.

When we arrived the preacher was on his knees, praying before a table on which there was a lantern—one he had obviously brought from Long Cay. He prayed fast and loud, and as he called on the Lord he punctuated his requests for blessings by banging the palm of his hand on the table. With each bang the lantern moved closer to the edge. Finally one slam sent it rolling on the floor and it went out.

The preacher's pitch and tempo never changed as he called, "Wait a minute, oh Lord, till I light de lantern." He struck a match, and as he did he shouted, "Let there be light!" And there was light. After which he announced the song: "Let the Lower Lights Be Burning," quite naturally.

Perhaps because of my visit to the church, the old local preacher called on me next day. In the course of our conversation he remarked that because of his failing eyesight he could no longer read the Bible. This was a common complaint among the older out-islanders. On my visit to Acklins with Commissioner Pyfrom two years before I had heard it several times. Consequently on this visit I had brought along several pairs of old glasses given me by friends in Madison. Now I selected one and told the preacher to try them on.

He looked through them at his Bible. "Praise the Lord!" he cried. "I preach de same sermon every Sunday for twenty years because I can't see de Good Book. Now by de Grace of

God and dis spec, I can preach a new sermon next Sunday."

The Pentecostals were not the only denomination at Landrail Point. Of a population of about seventy, approximately forty were Seventh Day Adventists, the rest divided almost evenly between Pentecostals and Baptists. There was also a Church of England and at one time, I was told, there had been five members: the schoolteacher and his wife, the ancient catechist and his wife, and a half-witted girl. But the schoolteacher and his wife had been transferred, the catechist had died, and the half-witted girl had been sent to Nassau. However, the church still stood open and one Sunday morning I stopped to look in.

Before a church of absolutely empty pews, attired in her Sunday dress, stood the catechist's wife. Faithfully the old lady was going through the entire service. When I moved quietly forward and sat down she did not seem to notice. When I took part in the responsive reading she never blinked. At the end of the service she greeted me as if accustomed to having visitors every Sunday and told me when the next service would be held. I almost hated to admit to her that I was not a member.

My friend Frank Scavella, who was the lay preacher for the Seventh Day Adventists, owned the "larger" of the two stores at Landrail Point. The other was owned by a Baptist. My first Saturday at Landrail Point I went to Frank's store to do my weekend shopping. "Oh, but, Mr. Cottman," he said in a distressed voice, "this is our Sabbath. I cannot sell on the Sabbath."

I looked dismayed and he added quickly, "But you are hungry and in need of food. I can *give* you what you need today."

I thought he meant he could give it to me today and I could pay him for it the next day. But when I tried to pay I found I was wrong. When he had said he could give it to me, he meant *give*. After that I learned that if I needed to shop on Saturdays, I went to the Baptist store. On Sunday I could go to the Seventh Day Adventist. In that way we had a store open every day of the week.

The trouble was that on most days of the week neither of

them had much of anything to sell. Food was a problem at Landrail Point just as on most of the out-islands. Canned foods had to be ordered from Nassau. They were expensive and the tiny settlement stores could not afford to keep them stocked. Home-grown food was cheap but scarce. Eggs were only a penny apiece, but Cyril or I had to go from door to door seeking them, and rarely getting more than one at a place. Sometimes the lady would say, "I got no egg now, but de fowl is on de nest. When she done finish I send de egg over by de little boy." Strangely, chickens were more plentiful than eggs. I could almost always buy a hen for a shilling, or a frier for half that. Sometimes a small head of cabbage or a few tomatoes would be available, but such things were rare treats. The natives of the out-islands so rarely eat fresh vegetables they simply don't know enough about them to care.

I had figured it would take two weeks at best to hear from Mr. McKinney at Nassau about the purchase of Gun Bluff. Because my vacation time was short, the wait seemed long. One day Frank Scavella told me, "I am going to Pompey Bay on Acklins tonight in the *Grace*. If you and Cyril would like to go, you would be most welcome." He planned to leave just before midnight to catch the tide.

About 11 P.M. Cyril and I walked down to the rocks where the *Grace* was tied. Frank and his son Hartman were already there, getting ready to load. The *Grace* was a fourteen-foot dinghy with a sail. It was wide for its length. Even so, it seemed absolutely impossible that all the stuff piled on the rocks would ever go into or onto it. There were bags of coconuts, citrus, charcoal, yams, corn, cassava; there were two crates of chickens, a goat, a rocking chair, all kinds of pots and cooking utensils. There were bundles upon bundles of sugar cane. I stared at it all and shook my head. Even if Frank piled it all on the boat, where would he get the four of us?

I was pondering this when people began to appear out of the darkness. First there was a man alone, then a couple, then another and another, all carrying suitcases, rolls of bedding, boxes of food. Apparently all the Scavellas and their sisters

62

and their cousins and their aunts had turned out for the free ride. By the time Frank was ready to load it developed that the crew and passengers would number eleven instead of four.

I was the first object placed aboard. Then, under Frank's direction, there grew around me a solid barricade of freight. It mounted higher and higher until I could see over the top only in some places. Rope after rope was passed over the cargo and tied to the gunwale on each side. If anything happens, I thought, my lot is cast with the *Grace* forever. I'll never get out.

Then came the passengers with their personal belongings. They swarmed over the cargo; they filled in the notches I had been able to see over, and piled on top. Finally Hartman climbed over the passengers to the mast. Frank took the tiller. The sail went up and we were off.

The moon was not yet quite down. I could tell because, looking straight up, I could still see light in the sky. Then the light faded, leaving only the stars. There was a gentle breeze; the sea was calm (praise the Lord!) and the *Grace* moved slowly before it, her gunwale within inches of the water. To pass the time, and possibly to keep awake so they would not fall off, the passengers began to sing hymns. I wondered what some German submarine commander would think if he should suddenly pop up from beneath the water to see and hear this strange object floating on the surface.

We had been sailing about an hour when we reached the cut between Crooked Island and Acklins. Here the tide runs strongly, and as we came closer even I could feel the *Grace* picking up speed. Also I could see Hartman standing by the mast and peering into the darkness ahead. Suddenly he began to scream, "Keep off, Papa! Keep off! You too close to Old Woman!" In the same moment a huge rock loomed close above us.

The *Grace* veered. The rock slid past and out of sight. When I could get my heart out of my mouth I asked a man sitting just above me what was the Old Woman. "Jus' a big rock," he said. "Peoples do say a old woman lived there one time."

There were no more adventures en route. Incredible as it

seemed, the *Grace* with her amazing cargo reached Pompey Bay safely and two days later returned the same way. Waiting for me was a letter from Mr. McKinney of Nassau. He would sell me the ten acres around Gun Bluff, including 500 feet of ocean front, for ten pounds, or $40.00.

I had already made an agreement with Fred Scavella to build a stone kitchen eight by twelve feet with a thatched roof for eight pounds. So now that I had the letter from Mr. McKinney, work started immediately. The first thing, Fred said, was to build a lime kiln.

Several hundred buttonwood logs were cut and some of them arranged in a circle, like spokes emanating from a wheel. Then a vast amount of native limestone was broken into egg-sized pieces. A layer of this, approximately eighteen inches deep, was poured over the buttonwood logs. Another layer of logs was added, then another layer of limestone, and so on until the whole thing stood about three feet high and ten feet in diameter. In the center, the hub, a hole about eight inches wide was left. This was filled with some kind of inflammable material and set afire. The heat of the burning logs converted the limestone into quicklime. This in turn needed only water to make it into the lime which, along with sand, water, and rock, is the basic building material of Crooked Island.

Of these the only problem was water. Salt water, according to Fred Scavella, could not be used. The nearest fresh water was two miles away. At this point Harry McKinney, the postmaster, said he might be able to help. He knew, he said, how to use a divining rod.

I had heard of this method of finding water, but I had never seen anyone do it. Certainly it did not seem very scientific. On the other hand I have never been one to scoff at something merely because it appears to be superstition. If Harry McKinney could find water, then I was all for it, no matter what method he used.

So with his little boy Willis tagging after us, we left Landrail Point one morning at daylight and walked to Gun Bluff. Mr. McKinney cut a forked stick from one of the scrubby bushes that grew just back from the beach. Then he began to walk, trailing the forked end of the stick behind him. He had gone perhaps 200 yards when the stick turned over. It just turned over, as if somebody had taken the other end and twisted it. "Here the place," Mr. McKinney said.

He put down the forked stick and, using the shovel he had brought along, began to dig. Two feet down he hit water. "Try the water, Willis," Mr. McKinney said.

Willis lay down and scooped up a handful of water and tasted it. "Fresh, Papa. It fresh fresh."

I sighed, both pleased and baffled. But when I asked McKinney how the divining rod worked he said, "You just dig where the stick turn over."

"I know," I said. "But what makes it turn over?"

He shook his head. "I don't know. I just walk along dragging it, and where it turn over you get water."

Which was all I ever learned about that.

The big trouble with Mr. McKinney's stick was it had turned over a good quarter of a mile away and downhill from where I wanted my kitchen. Scavella had hired several women and children to carry sand from the beach up the bluff to the kiln. Now they had to carry the water even farther.

It was about this time that I crossed the island one day to Colonel Hill, the settlement I had visited with Mr. Whylly two years before. I called on John Deleveaux whose uncle happened to be present. During the conversation I mentioned that I had bought Gun Bluff.

Deleveaux's uncle was a very old man with eyes like a bird's. "You find the well?" he asked me.

"What well?"

"You found the rock quarry?"

I had. I passed it each time I went up and down the bluff to the beach. "All right," the old man said. "I tell you something I bet nobody else alive know about. Back in 1873 the government started building that big lighthouse out on Bird Rock and use the quarry at Gun Bluff. We work for three years on that lighthouse, and the men in the quarry need drinking water. So the government dug them a well. To find it you go down the beach about one hundred feet east of the quarry, then turn back into the bush about a hundred feet."

Next day at Gun Bluff I took a machete and I went exploring. And there was the well just where he had said. It was about six feet in diameter and fifteen feet deep, cut down through solid rock. The bottom was filled with debris and no water was showing. But a fig tree grew just to one side; from it a long adventitious root plunged down to the bottom of the well. Unless there was water that root would not have been there.

I went back up the bluff to where Scavella and his crew were working. "Mr. Cottman—" he greeted me, as he had been doing for some time now—"when I contract for this kitchen, I don't know I was going to have to tote water all the way from Kingdom Come."

"Oh, don't worry about it," I said. "If you'd rather have a closer well, I'll find one for you."

He grinned unhappily. "I only wish you could."

"It shouldn't be any trouble," I said. "I'm pretty good at that sort of thing." I walked out of sight, then came back a couple of minutes later. "I found you a well."

"I wish you was telling the truth, Mr. Cottman."

"I am. Come on and I'll show you."

It took some persuading, but Fred and a couple of his helpers followed me down past the quarry. I showed them the well and they all three stood silently gazing down into it. "Well now that is something," Fred said finally. "All the peoples working here been living on Crooked Island all their lives and not one of 'em know 'bout this well. Then this man come from off and go straight to the well. How you find this well, Mr. Cottman?"

"I just followed my nose," I told him. "I can smell fresh water, if there's any around."

Fred's helper shook his head in awe. "Dot one wonderful mon!" he said. "One wonderful mon!"

It was the first time I had heard the expression, and it was

66

spoken in such absolute sincerity that my conscience would not let me go on with the joke. I had to confess the truth. Even then, the fact I had learned something about their island which none of them knew seemed wonderful enough. Buckets and shovels and ropes were fetched. Two men climbed down into the well and started to clean it out. Within a few minutes water began to spring.

From this point on the kitchen progressed rapidly. Even so, I could not stay to see it finished. Work had just started on the walls when it was time for me to go back to my classroom. Leaving the work in Fred's hands, I got passage on the *Lady May* for Nassau.

The boat was loaded with the usual out-island cargo. There were about twenty-five crates of chickens. Most of these were roosters and they crowed continuously, day and night. Also there were six sheep and a big hog tied forward.

The captain assigned me to the right-hand side of the cabin. This was divided by a central aisle with two bunks on each side. These bunks were side by side, the second far back under the deck and could be reached only by crawling over the first one.

I went below and tossed my baggage onto the bunk back under the deck. Opposite me across the aisle sat a frightened-looking old lady. She had her eyes closed and was praying steadily, half aloud. On the bunk behind her something moved in the darkness, and when I looked closely I saw an enormous black woman with a bandanna wrapped around her head. She lay stretched out on her back and filled the entire space between the bunk and the deck overhead.

It was already late evening so I too stretched out and tried to sleep. But overhead the roosters were crowing, and as the *Lady May* began to roll the old lady across from me began to pray in earnest. Behind her the fat woman began to snore, the two mingling into a kind of strange duet with a rooster accompaniment. "O-o-oh Lord!" the old lady would call in a high quivering voice. Then in a lower one, "O-o-oh Lord, fetch us a good course to Nassau. Carry us over de briny deep. Bring

67

us safe into de harbor." The roosters would crow; the snore would reach a crescendo and fade away. "Ah Lord!" the old lady would pray. "Save us, Lord, save us!"

It went on and on. Sometimes the snores would change in pitch; the roosters varied their cries somewhat. But the old lady had one good prayer and she stayed with it. Eventually I slept a little.

The next day was beautiful with a light wind. A long gentle swell caused the *Lady May* to roll slightly but not enough to make me sick. The two women ventured on deck, the fat one stretching out on the port side, café au lait on the starboard. Each time the starboard side dipped, café au lait would utter a quavery, high-pitched, "Ah Jesus!" Then as the port side dipped there would come from beneath the bandanna a deep-toned, reassuring, "Ah Lord!" Between times the roosters crowed.

The second night I decided to try my chances on deck. In the center of the forward part of the deck there was a hatch which formed a little plateau about eighteen inches above the deck. It made a nice bed, though narrow. Tied along the side of this and standing on the deck were the six sheep. Tied at the forward end, where my head would go, was the hog. I lay down, put some straw under my head, and was quite comfortable. Each time the boat rolled the sheep would obligingly crowd against my bed and keep me from falling off. This is going to be fine, I thought, and was almost asleep when the sheep near the foot of my bed began to nibble on my big toe. I kicked him carefully and deliberately in the flank. He backed off and looked at me with a hurt expression. "Well, keep your big fat mouth off my feet," I told him, and lay back.

This caught the attention of the sheep at the head of the bed. He stared as if he had never seen a man before. Slowly he brought his face closer and closer to mine, looking me straight in the eye with a kind of dazed intentness. Perhaps he was disappointed in what he saw, or simply disgusted, or maybe allergic to people. Abruptly, his face not three inches from mine, he sneezed violently.

68

I retired to the boat's rail and washed my face, then came back to bed, this time looking the other way. And now it was the hog. He switched his tail across my face several times, dusting it off possibly, then started to use the top of my head as a back-scratcher. I slapped and pushed but he seemed to take this as a gesture of affection and snuggled closer.

My shirt at this time was fastened with a safety pin in lieu of buttons that had popped off sometime in the past. I unfastened the safety pin and let the hog have it, up to the hilt. It was the end of our romance. He moved over and molested me no more.

We were scheduled under normal conditions to reach Nassau in three days, and just at noon on the third day we sighted the water tower. At the same time the wind died. There wasn't even a swell. We lay for hours, as still as Coleridge's "painted ship upon a painted ocean." As evening came on, the crew started taking turns sculling, with progress so slow I couldn't tell it was progress at all. Nobody slept that night. Sometime after dark the man sculling began to sing. The others, including the two female passengers, sang with him. The song I remember was to the tune of "She'll Be Coming Round the Mountain" and the first lines of the various stanzas went like this:

> *Oh the good ship Zion when she comes . . .*
> *King Jesus will be captain when she comes . . .*
> *De angels will be sailors when she comes . . .*
> *De saints will be de passengers when she comes . . .*
> *De Bible will be cargo when she comes . . .*

And so, at long last, ah Lord, we fetched us a good course into Nassau and a safe harbor, and I took an airplane back to Madison and long days teaching biology and chemistry. But behind me was a little piece of the Bahamas that belonged to me and to which I would return.

8

Of Sand Flies and
Paradise

I LIVED through that winter and with early June was back
in Nassau. I had written Mrs. Whylly the date of my arrival
and she had promised to have the *Lady May* waiting for me.
It was, ready to sail in two days. I spent those shopping for
lumber and other building materials and food.

There were the usual headwinds but the sea was not rough.
I didn't even get seasick and we made Crooked Island in five
days. It looked as though this summer everything was going
my way.

At Landrail Point I went ashore and rounded up a crowd
of men and boys to help unload my materials; then we all sailed
around the point and anchored in the little bight under Gun
Bluff.

I couldn't wait for the unloading. I ran down the beach and
up the path that led past the quarry to the top of the bluff.
And there sat my brand-new little stone kitchen, bright and
white under the glare of the sun.

I pushed the door open and went in. The fireplace was
ready, but the room itself, of course, was totally empty. There
was no bed, no table, no chairs, just the floor of packed coral.
Yet it looked wonderful to me, even if right at the moment it
was extremely hot.

The crowd from the *Lady May* began to arrive, bringing up
the lumber and nails and crates of tinned foods and suitcases.

Most of this they put inside the kitchen on the floor. The rest was stacked outside against the wall. Then we all took the boat back to Landrail Point.

There was almost no wind and the trip took a long time. On the way Harry McKinney, the postmaster, told me that several days before there had been a short, violent cloudburst on Crooked Island. Since then there had been no more rain and very little wind. "And when the wind don't blow," he said, "it can be hot."

I mopped my brow and said I had noticed that.

Also it now turned out that the little house I had rented the summer before from McKinney's sister was occupied. He didn't know of any place in the community that was for rent. This didn't bother me because I planned to live in my kitchen at Gun Bluff. However, I would need some place to sleep tonight. After pondering this McKinney said I could sleep on the floor of the post office, if I wished. He could get me some gunnysacks—crocus sacks they are called in the Bahamas—for a bed.

He also brought me a Flit gun filled with kerosene because, he said, the sand flies and mosquitoes were unusually bad. He even advised that I keep the doors and windows (screens were simply unknown on Crooked Island) tight shut. I did, for a while. The air was stifling. Sweat ran out of me. It soaked the crocus sacks. It crawled down my skin in big thick drops like worms.

Finally I couldn't take it. I got up and opened a window and stuck my head outside—into a mass of hungry sand flies and mosquitoes. I jerked my head back in, and they came in with it. I was naked, and they swarmed all over me. It felt as though I had been sprayed with a Flit gun full of acid.

I slammed the window shut, grabbed the Flit gun McKinney had brought, and turned it on myself, thereby superimposing a layer of kerosene over the layer of sand flies over the layer of clammy sweat that already covered me. This stopped the stinging, but left me hotter than ever.

All night I waged war, first with the sand flies and mos-

71

quitoes, then with heat and asphyxiation from kerosene fumes. Dawn brought a little relief. Harry McKinney came with some jelly coconuts for my breakfast. As I scooped out the jelly he told me about an old man named Uncle Shad Sweeting who wanted a job at Gun Bluff. He was, McKinney said, too old for heavy work but he could help with the chores, he was a pretty good cook, and he was dependable. I agreed to give Uncle Shad a chance.

He was to report that afternoon. Meanwhile I walked back to Gun Bluff and set to work building something that could be used as a kitchen table in the daytime and a bed at night. The day was fiercely hot. Also the sand flies, which are not supposed ever to cause trouble during sunlit hours, were still bad. By the time Uncle Shad arrived in the late afternoon my disposition was not at its best.

He was a very old man with a slow smile on his dark face that showed most of his teeth missing. "You want some supper, Mr. Cottman?" he asked.

I did. I had not yet unpacked any cooking utensils, but Uncle Shad said that was all right. From a bag he had brought with him he took an old tin can, blackened by much use. Into this he poured some water, stirred in a little flour, and sat the mixture in the fireplace.

Here I should explain that on Crooked Island there are many fireplaces, but no chimneys. A fireplace is simply a raised place in the floor, usually about two by three feet in size and eighteen inches high, made of rocks plastered smooth with lime and sand. The fire is built on this, and the smoke—at least on good days—is gone with the trade wind.

I was working on my combination bed and table and paid little attention to Uncle Shad's cooking until he told me supper was ready. Supper, it seemed, was the stuff in the can. "Dis flour pop," he told me. "Plenty good."

I did not share Uncle Shad's delight in flour pop. To me it tasted like uncooked pancake batter. But just as I reconciled myself to a night of hunger Uncle Shad left the kitchen to re-

72

turn a few minutes later with his hat full of the ugliest-looking land crabs I have ever seen.

And they turned out to be delicious.

It was almost dusk now. All afternoon as the shadows had lengthened the sand flies had strengthened. By twilight they filled the air like smoke. I took off the shorts I had been wearing and put on long pants. The sand flies got inside the legs. I put on socks and pulled them over the bottoms of the trousers. I put on a long-sleeved sweater. I pulled another pair of socks over my hands for gloves. The sand flies still swarmed over my face. They burrowed through my hair and trepanned into my skull with red-hot augers. I pulled a shirt over my head, tucked the tails under the collar of the sweater, and wrapped the rest about my face with only the eyes and nose exposed. The sand flies got up my nose. I had to make adjustments, breathing through the cloth.

In this mummylike getup I sprinkled straw on my new table and went to bed. Uncle Shad had put some boards on the floor and covered them with crocus sacks for his bed. He put green wood on the fire to make smoke, closed the doors and windows, and retired for the night.

It was quite a night. Uncle Shad alternately groaned and snored. I just groaned.

Next morning the sand flies persisted. It was impossible to think about work. I went to the beach and the sand flies followed. I went swimming. Every time I had to lift my face out of the water they swarmed over me. They kept burrowing into my scalp. I got out of the water and put on all the clothing I had worn during the night. Sweat made it stick to me and the sand flies bit through it.

I had, as my aunt once pointed out to me, been proud of my ability to take it. But by the end of my third night on Crooked Island that summer, I'd had enough. I was willing to quit. I was ready to give up and go home. But there was no way to go. There would be no opportunity to get away until the next mailboat, which would be another week. Meanwhile I could suffer and try to survive.

73

It went on for five days and nights. It was impossible to sleep, except briefly through sheer exhaustion. It was almost impossible to eat. I had the hours numbered awaiting the arrival of the mailboat. I was through with Crooked Island forever.

And then about midnight of the fifth night a strange thing happened. There was no wind; yet the air itself seemed to change and take on a cool freshness. The sand flies withdrew, without apparent reason. I went to sleep and slept hard the rest of the night.

When I awoke the sun was shining but the air was cool. I opened the door and was greeted by a breeze that was refreshing beyond description. I went back into the kitchen and opened all the windows. The wind poured in like water. The smoke and stale air blew out. Not a sand fly remained. The hell I had endured for five days was suddenly changed to something akin to heaven, and all my first love for Gun Bluff and for all of Crooked Island came surging back. Leave on the mailboat? Don't be silly!

I began now to make plans in earnest for my house. Fred Scavella had another job, but he recommended a boss carpenter and mason I could hire for eighty cents a day. Other labor was no problem. Men came from all over Crooked Island begging for work at 2/6 (fifty cents) a day. Women and boys would work for thirty cents. Soon I was operating what looked like a private WPA project.

The house began to take shape. There was to be a large living room, twelve by twenty-five feet; a small hurricane room, eight by twelve with walls eighteen inches thick; another room thirteen by sixteen.

Early one morning I had a caller—a boy of about fourteen with the most absolutely ebony-hued skin I have ever seen. He introduced himself as Raphael and said he wanted a job as houseboy. He would work for a pound a month, he said.

He was obviously a bright youngster. I hired him—and immediately my life on Crooked Island became less complicated. For one thing I no longer had to live on flour pop, land crabs,

74

and food out of tins. Raphael would ask what I wanted for dinner and I would say, "Can you get any fresh vegetables?"

"I cannot rightly say, suh. But I tink Mr. Frank have one cabbage."

I would give him a bit of change and he would go off to Landrail Point, to be back about three hours later with his basket overflowing. Chickens, eggs, pigeon peas, watermelons, sweet potatoes, grapefruit, forbidden fruit, and bananas were often on our menu. There was even an occasional cabbage, roasting ears, and tomatoes. But the amazing thing was the way the money lasted. With frying chickens ten cents each, watermelons five cents, and other things in proportion, I could feed Uncle Shad, Raphael, and myself for less than a dollar a day; the only expensive items were the tinned foods I had brought from Nassau.

One morning I asked Raphael if he could get any fish. "Oh yes, suh," he said. "Mr. Frank has plenty fish."

With water all around us, I'd had no fish all that summer and I looked forward to it. But the thing Raphael served didn't taste like fish to me. It tasted more like tainted leather. "What is this?" I asked. "It's terrible!"

Raphael looked puzzled. "It taste good to me." But after a moment his face began to clear. "Maybe you likes *fresh* fish?"

"Of course I like fresh fish. What kind is this?"

"Dis corned fish. Peoples on Crooked Island likes fish hung in de sun and dried and rubbed wid salt. Peoples here don't eat fresh fish if we can get it corned."

"All right," I told him. "Only don't ever bring me any more of it."

"Yes, suh." But he remained baffled by the fact I did not prefer their great delicacy "corned fish and corned conchs."

Meanwhile, although the house grew rapidly the summer waned even faster. When it was time for me to leave, the walls were up but not the roof. I was faced with a problem.

One of my best workers that summer was a man named John McKinney—no relation of either the McKinney from whom I bought Gun Bluff or the postmaster. I made a deal

75

with him. For one pound a month he would supervise the rest of the building of my house, then act as caretaker.

I left for Nassau on a boat named the *Content,* a very suitable name for my mood at the end of that summer. She was a converted yacht and quite luxurious for the out-island trade. At least she was at first. Then we stopped at Long Island where the commissioner's wife came aboard with a crowd of children. These quickly discovered the shower bath and stayed there until the fresh-water tanks were empty. This left no water for drinking, washing, or cooking and altered the contented mood of some of us, including the captain.

9

These Are Pious Creatures

By the spring of 1943 war restrictions were such that I didn't know if I would be allowed to travel outside the U.S. Also, my draft status was in doubt. I had an aunt who was dependent on me, and I was beyond the preferred age for draftees. Then another birthday and a change in the draft law put me over the limit. My validated passport arrived and I departed.

In Nassau I learned that the *Content* had just left and would not make another trip for three weeks. The *Lady May* was laid up for repairs. Once more I had to search the waterfront for some local craft to carry me to Gun Bluff.

What I found was the *G. H. Almina* from Acklins, a twenty-four-foot sloop, only a little larger than the cheerless *Cheerful.* The captain, however, assured me she was unusually steady and comfortable, and there would be plenty of room. He did not tell me, and I did not know until I was ready to go aboard, that she was to carry ten other passengers, plus a heavy load of freight.

The passenger list included two women and the cabin was assigned to "de two females and de white gentleman." I knew, from having inspected it previously, there were only two narrow bunks with an aisle between them and I wondered just how it was to be converted into sleeping space for three. When I went below I saw the aisle had been filled with bags of flour right up to the level of the bunks, making the entire cabin into one wide bed. I had the port side, one lady slept in the middle and one on the starboard. The rest of the passengers slept catch-as-catch-can.

Except for my companions the trip was reminiscent of that on the *Cheerful*. There were the steady headwinds, the incessant tacking, the constant crazy pitch and roll, and seasickness. Within a few hours all my strength and energy had gone over the rail. I lay in a kind of torpid nausea, sometimes—but only sometimes—too inert to be sick. It seemed to me that most of my hours were spent wondering dully what time it was. My watch was in my pocket but to get it out and look at it required an act of will power and physical effort so great I could rarely manage it.

It took six days to reach the south end of Long Island. In that time I ate very little. Most of the food I had brought went untouched and grew moldy. I knew that I ought to eat. I would reason with myself that I had to get up and eat something in order to exist. But I couldn't bring myself to it.

The two women were in much the same condition. Consequently the cabin, hot and with little ventilation, was not an altogether desirable place; all of us avoided it most of the time. But one day when the boat was temporarily under the lee of some small cays, the rolling stopped, we were all in the cabin together, and we all felt better. I had managed to eat a whole biscuit.

At this point one of the ladies produced an old hymnbook and the two of them began to sing—the most wailful, lugubrious music I have ever listened to. After a few songs they

77

politely asked me to join them. I am not a good songster, but in this case that did not seem to matter; and I was rather flattered to be asked. So the three of us crouched with our heads together over a tattered hymnal and howled. On my part, at least, it was a kind of prayer that we might be permitted to remain forever where we were and peacefully starve to death.

It was not to be. We moved out from back of the cay, and shortly after that—it was 9 P.M. on the sixth day—we cleared the south end of Long Island and reached the Crooked Island Passage. Immediately I felt the difference in the movement of the boat. The short, choppy bucking of the last six days was replaced by the great, long, elevatorlike rise and fall of deep ocean swells.

The captain stuck his head in the cabin. "I'll have you over to Crooked Island in the morning, boss," he said cheerfully.

I blessed him—but too soon. The wind was still dead ahead and with morning there was no sight of land. All day the *Almina* beat against an ever-increasing headwind. There was plenty of motion, but it was all either up and down or back and forth. None of it was forward. When darkness closed in there was still no land in sight. But great purple and black clouds, split now and then by lightning, were piling up in the south.

About 8 o'clock the first squall broke, followed by a more violent one two hours later. All eleven passengers were now crowded into the cabin. The hatch and skylights were tightly closed, the cabin illuminated only by a smoky lantern swung from the overhead.

The first two squalls were mere curtain raisers for the one that struck at midnight. It hit as suddenly as a blow, and it shook loose everything on deck and in the cabin. The wind shrieked, the thunder roared, the *Almina* pitched and rolled, people and baggage rolled in the little space there was to roll. Women screamed and children cried and in the occasional moments of semi-silence in the cabin we could hear barrels rolling overhead and the unintelligible shouting of the crew.

I was lying on my bunk, pushed over as far as I could get

against the side of the boat. Alongside me three men sat with their knees drawn up against their chins. A box of some sort was pushing against the top of my head and a suitcase had fallen across my legs. If the *Almina* went down I was going down with it because it was impossible for me to move.

About this time I discovered that although the cabin was airtight, it was not watertight. In the deck, directly over my face, there was a nail hole. Through this a steady trickle of water began to flow. It was dirty deck water and from the texture I wondered if it had passed through a pig or chicken coop before it reached me. It fell right in my face, and wedged in as I was I could not move.

I did manage to turn my head to the side. And there, within an arm's reach, was the answer to my problem. It was an old and battered chamber pot. Where it had come from and to whom it belonged I never knew, or cared. With much straining, and by twisting one arm to the breaking point, I reached it. To my delight it fit perfectly into the space between my forehead and the deck overhead. The water now ran into the pot and not my face.

The two women had become hysterical and were screaming steadily. A small boy thought he heard the crew shout, "She's going down!" and tried to tear open the hatch. A man jerked him away from it; another hit him over the head with a board, knocking him cold. I lay quietly sick, with the chamber pot balanced on my forehead.

Then it began to overflow. I punched the man sitting against my shoulder. As best he could he looked back. I asked, "Do you think you could move this and empty it?"

He evaluated the situation. "Well, sir, I be glad to try."

It took some doing, but he got the pot. There was no place to empty it, except on the flour sacks where he was sitting, so he emptied it there and passed it back to me. I wedged it in place again. The night and the storm went on.

Somewhere around 4 A.M. the squall ended. Shortly afterward the captain opened the hatch and stuck his head into the cabin. "Boss man," he said, "we get blow off course. We is most into Long Cay." Then he asked if I would object if he put me ashore on Long Cay and took his other passengers on to Acklins. He would return, he said, in two or three days and take me to Gun Bluff.

Would I object? I wouldn't have objected if he had put me on the top of Mount Everest as long as it was ashore.

The settlement at Long Cay is located on the north side where there is high ground and a beautiful beach, but no harbor. It was impossible to land there. The harbor and dock is on the south side, and just about dawn I was put ashore there. Nearby was a little government warehouse. One of the crew put my baggage in the warehouse and I was left alone. No people live on the south side and it is a two-mile walk across the island to the settlement.

I had been almost constantly seasick for eight days. In that time I had eaten little and lost more. The last night hadn't helped. My outraged sense of balance was still playing tricks on me and for a while I had to lean against the wall of the warehouse to stay upright.

Slowly I extracted my money and passport from my baggage. Carrying them and leaving the rest of my belongings in the warehouse, I started across the island. It was a long two miles. Now and then I had to sit down and rest or take hold of a tree to keep the earth from tilting up and hitting me in the face. But finally I reached the Whyllys. I slumped down on the doorstep. "Mrs. Whylly," I called weakly.

From upstairs came a sleepy voice. "Who dot?"

"I done reach," I said.

The voice came sharply to life. "Who dot is?" A moment later Mrs. Whylly's head popped out of the upstairs window and she stared down at me. I held onto the floor to keep it from falling from under me and grinned faintly back at her.

So it was as it had been after the *Cheerful:* a big kettle of water heating for a bath while I explained what had happened; hot, delicious food that I could keep down; a bed that didn't move.

For two days I lived at the guest house, ate Mrs. Whylly's

80

excellent cooking, and rested. Then the *Almina* returned, the weather was calm, and I moved on to Crooked Island.

There had been some changes made atop Gun Bluff. John McKinney had planted a field of green corn close to my kitchen. His mother had set out zinnias and hibiscus and they were heavy with blooms. There was even some grass.

The house itself was finished, but empty of furniture, and the first thing I set out to build for myself was a bed. Remembering the week-of-the-sand-fly, I fashioned a sort of cage on legs. The cage was three feet high, thirty inches wide, and six feet four inches long. The two ends, the top, and one side were covered with a double thickness of cheesecloth. The open side had a detachable frame, also covered with cheesecloth. If there were sand flies or mosquitoes, all I had to do was insert the frame and they couldn't get at me.

My mattress was a tick, which I had brought with me, filled with "bed grass." This is a soft grass that grows abundantly on Crooked Island. The natives all use it, and it makes a very comfortable bed indeed.

Now with a bed and kitchen there remained only one other necessity before I got around to luxuries. This was a shower bath, and I had come prepared with a sprinkling can. I built a box four inches high and just large enough to hold the can snugly; this I hinged to a platform slightly higher than my head. Using a rope and pulley I could tilt the can forward to pour water over me, then pull it back into place. It worked beautifully.

I had also brought a wheelbarrow, an item that delighted Uncle Shad. When he first saw it he actually clapped his hands calling to everyone around to come and look. "Papa Cottman done fetch a buggy!"

(I might pause here to explain that among Crooked Islanders the title "Papa" is one of both deference and friendship. When Uncle Shad, who was old enough to be my papa, and Raphael and the Scavella brothers and some others started to call me Papa I was honestly quite proud. I felt now I belonged.)

Using Uncle Shad's "buggy," I began to put in a lawn and some citrus trees. In many places the top of the bluff was nothing but bare rock. A short distance away, however, there were pockets of good soil. We hauled buggy-loads of it to mix with seaweed, which makes an excellent fertilizer, and in a short time had a foundation for a lawn. After this Uncle Shad took it on himself to build a sea wall along the open side of the old quarry. At one time in his life he had been a stone mason and now, using loose rock, he fashioned a wall three feet wide, six feet high, and about seventy-five feet long. He was very proud of it. "Papa," he told me, "dis wall be here plenty hundreds of years after I am dust. Whenever you look at dis wall, you think of Uncle Shad."

"You're tougher than that wall," I told him. "You'll outlast it."

He shook his head. "I am eighty years old. Dot's already three score and ten, and den some."

Between Gun Bluff and Landrail Point there was an area known as Marine Farm where Mr. McKinney (the Nassau McKinney) kept some cows pastured. They were native stock, big, gaunt creatures that looked like Texas longhorns. Even so, I regarded them with yearning. The one thing I missed most in the islands was fresh milk.

One day looking at these cows, I asked Harry McKinney, caretaker for the other McKinney, "Are they cross?"

He looked puzzled. So I tried to put my question into Crooked Island dialect. "Is the cows rude?"

"O-oh!" he said. "No, sur. These cows wouldn't hurt nobody. They is very pious creatures."

Immediately I had a mental image of them, dressed in their best Sunday bonnets, filing into church. And so, assured of their gentle piety, I arranged to borrow one for milking. She stood perfectly still while I put a rope around her neck. When I pulled on the rope she remained perfectly still. I pulled harder. She planted her feet and did not budge.

My family had owned a cow when I was a boy and that one I had been able to lead around by a ring in her nose. Now I hooked my thumb in one nostril of this pious creature and my third finger in the other and pulled gently. It worked like a charm. Without difficulty we proceeded to Gun Bluff.

The trouble started with milking time. I tied the cow to a tree, her head low. Cautiously I approached the milking place. I washed the udder. No trouble. Holding a tin cup in my left hand, I gingerly took hold of a teat with my right hand and squeezed. She kicked the tin cup a good twenty feet.

I called Raphael and together we managed to get both the cow's hind legs tied to a bush. But it was no good. Even tied, she managed to fling herself about like a Pentecostal in a holy fit, and I wondered if this could be what Mr. McKinney had meant by "pious." Then during a resting spell I noticed her eating a crabshell.

Great numbers of these can always be found in the bush and I told Raphael to fill a dishpan with them. "Now," I said, "you feed them to her while I milk."

Raphael proved almost as balky as the cow, but eventually he approached her, holding the dishpan at arm's length. The cow took the shells one by one and munched them contentedly; when I began to milk she didn't even notice. So I worked furiously for half an hour—and squeezed out almost half a cupful of milk. After this was strained through a cloth I had about three swallows left.

I kept the cow several days. There was no more fighting, but there was progressively less milk. Finally I branded the experiment a failure and took her home.

My next attempt was with a goat. There were plenty of goats around Landrail Point, though the natives never bothered to milk them. I selected a large black one with a big bag and an evil eye, and told the children of the owner I would pay them sixpence a pint for her milk.

They considered it a generous offer and began operations at once. The goat's objections were even more violent than the cow's had been. Not even crabshells would pacify her. Soon half the children of Landrail Point had assembled, some shouting instructions and some battling the goat. When she kicked, an entire posse grabbed each leg. The goat squatted, her belly against the ground. Two boys got astride and lifted her. A girl started to squeeze the milk into a can. The goat resisted, holding up the milk. Another girl slapped the udder, knocking the milk down. Eventually there was what we estimated to be a pint of milk.

The children agreed to bring the milk to me each morning. Containers were scarce, but I found a Klim can of unknown capacity they could use. That brought on the question of how much milk was a pint. I remembered there are 231 cubic inches in a gallon and that the volume of a cylinder is $\pi R^2 H$. So I did a little mathematics and came out with a nice clean stick calibrated to read in pennies and ha'pennies. Each morning when the milk came, all I had to do was dip my stick in it and read off the level of the milk in money, a process that both baffled and delighted the children.

So the summer passed while I drank milk and worked on my yard. I built a sundial. I built steps leading down to the beach. I even built, at the top of the bluff, two huge pillars eight feet high. They were plastered smooth and whitewashed, each with a depression at the top for a large flower pot. You could see them from all over the north end of Crooked Island and for miles out at sea.

Now, I thought, all I need is a boat.

10

Not a Boat But a Bride

DURING that winter of 1943–44 I tried to lay the groundwork for having a dinghy built. The best boat builders in the Bahamas were supposed to live on Abaco, one of the few Bahamian islands containing any large growth of timber. I wrote to the commissioner asking for information about builders and living accommodations. He answered promptly, giving me the names of several builders and stating that, although there were no hotels on the island, I might be able to secure a room at the home of Mrs. Ellen Sawyer in the settlement of Marsh Harbour.

I wrote to the builders and to Mrs. Ellen Sawyer. In due time I received answers; the one that intrigued me read:

Dear Mr. Cottman:
We have talked the matter over, and have decided to take you.
Yours truly,
Viola Sawyer

Obviously, I thought, here was a lady of few words. But whether she was Mrs. Ellen Sawyer's daughter or daughter-in-law, her sister-in-law or her mother-in-law I had no way of knowing. In answering I flipped a coin to decide whether to address her as Miss or Mrs., and decided on the latter.

Her next letter gave me the price of room and board by the week. It also referred to Mrs. Ellen Sawyer as "Mama" and I realized I had probably been mistaken about the Mrs.

It may be that I kept writing to Miss Viola Sawyer merely because it provided a diversion from the routine of teaching. I spent most of my time in Madison thinking about the Bahamas, and it was pleasant to have someone there to write to who wrote back brief but intelligent and interesting letters. Anyway, by spring I was explaining to her why I needed a dinghy, and how I planned to retire after two more years of teaching and live on Crooked Island. I even explained my dream of setting up a little laboratory at Gun Bluff to do experimental work on cold light.

Miss Sawyer wrote that she thought this a very worthwhile ambition. "You might make a discovery," she said, "that would benefit all mankind." It was an idea that flattered and pleased me.

It was in this same letter that she mentioned, with no en-

largement whatsoever, that she was "touched with deafness."
I wasn't sure exactly what she meant.

I was also writing an occasional letter to John McKinney at
Crooked Island and in one of them I asked how much it would
cost to build a barn at Gun Bluff. I can't recall precisely the
reason why I felt I had to have a barn. Perhaps I planned to
house in it the chickens I was always counting before they
hatched. He wrote that he could put up a plastered stone building, twelve by thirty-two feet, floored, with a thatched roof for
sixty-eight pounds. I told him to go ahead.

So that June when I reached Crooked Island I had not only
a house and a kitchen but a barn. Flowers bloomed all over
the place. John had planted another field of corn. There were
watermelons ripening in my front yard. Papaws hung heavy on
the trees. Now, truly, I had just about everything except a
dinghy. So I caught a passing boat to Nassau, and another
from there to Abaco.

I had, of course, written Miss Sawyer when to expect me.
She had written that I would save a good bit of time and sea
travel if I got off the mailboat at a landing called East Side.
From there a half-mile walk would take me across the island
to Marsh Harbour; the mailboat had to circle the entire east
corner of the island and did not reach Marsh Harbour until
several hours later.

There was quite a crowd of Nassau vacationers on the
Richard Campbell and a fair crowd on the dock to meet them.
We came ashore in a dinghy, and as we got closer I saw that,
unlike the Windward Islands, the population here, judged by
those on the dock, was predominantly white. There were quite
a few women, most of them dressed in brightly colored holiday
costumes.

I climbed out of the dinghy onto the dock, picked up my
suitcase, and looked uncertainly around me. A slender, rather
handsome white woman in her mid-thirties came toward me.
She had brown hair, bobbed and slightly curly. She was tall
and carried herself extremely well. The first thought that

crossed my mind was: She looks a good bit like the Duchess of Windsor.

"You are Mr. Cottman?" she asked.

"And you are Miss Sawyer?"

The crowd was moving away from the dock. There were no automobiles, not even a wagon or buggy. Everybody walked, and we walked with them along a narrow, unpaved road and over the crest of a steep hill. A scattering of houses showed ahead, and I remarked that all of these were of frame construction whereas the houses on Crooked Island were all of what the natives called "tabby lime." Miss Sawyer's answer had no relation to what I had said, and I realized she had not heard me. She was indeed "touched with deafness." Certain sounds she heard quite clearly; if she was looking directly at me she usually understood what I said. But some sounds she missed completely.

Yet she talked pleasantly, unhurriedly; most of her comments were about the things we were passing and needed no answer. The weather was hot, the road unshaded from the glare of the sun, my suitcase was heavy. Still, I was enjoying the walk.

I have now come to a part of my story that I find difficult to tell. It is quite easy for a man, writing about himself, to tell exactly when and why he became, let us say, seasick. It is far more difficult to explain exactly when and why he fell in love. At least it is for me. Looking back, there is the irrefutable evidence that it happened. But the details of how are hazy.

I had come to Abaco for a boat; yet I cannot now recall just what happened about that boat that summer. I remember Viola (I got past the "Miss Sawyer" business in a hurry) knew all three of the builders the commissioner had recommended, and I persuaded her to go with me to speak to each one of them. But I don't remember what I said to them. Somehow the dinghy had lost its importance. At least I was in no hurry to order one.

The Marsh Harbour area is a labyrinth of intermingling

land and water. Wherever you look there is some of both. The water is crystal clear and multicolored; in some places there are sand beaches and in some rocky bluffs rise sharply out of the bays. It is a wonderful country for picnics. Viola and I went on picnics. We went swimming. We would sit on the beach and eat picnic lunches Viola had prepared. She would watch my lips, the better to understand what I might be saying, and it gave me the feeling of being the complete center of her attention.

And I suppose those picnic lunches had something to do with it. Viola was (is, I am happy to say) an excellent cook. Her mother, Mrs. Ellen Sawyer, ran a small store and Viola kept the house. I remember one of my first impressions was that she did a fine job of housekeeping. The little cottage, not more than 150 feet from the water's edge, was spotlessly clean. And here Viola, as cook, had an amazing talent for preparing meals without any visible effort.

There were a great many visitors, practically all of them Viola's relatives. She was, it appeared, related to just about half the white population of Abaco. I met an intricate array of uncles, aunts, cousins, cousins-in-law, and cousins once and twice removed. While all these interwoven relatives came and went, Viola would be hostess; then (apparently without having even left the room more than once or twice for a few seconds at a time) she would announce the meal ready. And such meals! There were all kinds of native dishes I had not tasted before: stewed whelk, conch fritters, crawfish salad, baked shellfish. I loved them all.

I will not say that Viola's path to my heart lay through my stomach. Perhaps I liked the food because Viola had cooked it. As I have already admitted, my impressions of the fast waning days of that summer are hazy. But certainly both the days and nights had taken on a kind of golden tint that I found altogether wonderful.

I had, of course, been mildly in love on a number of previous occasions. There had even been times when I had vaguely considered marriage, but quickly thought better of it. I did

88

not consider myself the marrying kind. And the truth is that during those first days at Abaco I still didn't. I was, I told myself, a man who cherished his independence above all else.

Yet by the morning of August 3, exactly one week after my arrival at Marsh Harbour, my feelings had reached such a pitch that I knew I must talk with Viola, alone, and tell her how I felt. There was, however, no opportunity. All morning people kept dropping in, one after another. It wasn't until after the midday meal that we were alone in the house. Viola was washing dishes while I dried them.

"Viola—" I said. I put down the last cup. "Viola, let's go in the parlor and sit down. I want to talk to you."

"Let me put these away. I'll be there in a minute."

I went in the front room and waited. I heard Viola close the kitchen cabinet—and at the same time I heard somebody else open the kitchen door. There were voices. They went on. And on. Finally they ended. The kitchen door opened and closed again. Viola came in the front room. "Pearson was here to invite us to a picnic tomorrow. I told him we'd both like to go. You will, won't you?"

"All right. Viola—"

"Yes?"

"Sit down. I—"

The screen door flew open and Viola's thirteen-year-old cousin, Jeannette, came running in. "Viola," she panted, "they've sent a lot of those religious pictures from Nassau to the church in Dundas Town! Will you walk down with me to see them?"

"In this hot sun?"

"Please. It isn't far."

Viola turned to me. "You haven't been to Dundas Town. Would you like to walk down?"

I asked, without enthusiasm, "How far is it?"

"About a mile and a half."

Now I liked Jeannette. She was a nice little girl. Under ordinary circumstances I would have been glad to go with her and Viola. But the present circumstances were not ordinary.

Not for me, anyway. All day I had been planning things I wanted to say to Viola. But I wanted to say them to Viola alone.

She apparently misinterpreted my delay in answering. "It isn't so far, Evans. And Dundas Town is a pretty little settlement. I think you'll enjoy seeing it."

This was not how I had planned on spending the afternoon. But what else could I do? So we started for Dundas Town, and my frustrated mood had its physical repercussions. The sun had never been so hot. I broke into a sweat. My skin burned with prickly heat, probably engendered by my nettled disposition. Finally I stopped. "I don't want to go any farther. I'm going back home."

Viola asked with concern, "Do you feel bad?"

"I don't feel too good."

"We'll go back."

"But I want to see the pictures," Jeannette said.

"Well this needn't stop you," I said. "You can go right on by yourself. It isn't far."

"I don't want to go by myself. If you won't go, I'll go back with you."

In stony silence the three of us headed back toward the house. When we reached it, Jeannette hesitated. For one terrible moment I thought she was coming in. Then she tossed her head and walked off.

Viola and I went in the house. "I'd better go start supper," she said.

I must have made a groaning noise. Or maybe it was the look on my face that stopped her. "Evans," she said, "are you feeling all right?"

"I think so," I said. "It's just that all day long I have been trying to talk to you alone, and never a chance."

"Alone? What about?"

The question stopped me, for a moment. I knew what about all right; but the proper singing of love's old sweet song requires not only a setting but a mood, and I'd had a day of concentrated bafflement. There was still too much acid in my system. I needed time for the dregs to settle. Half turning away from her, I said, "About Gun Bluff."

"About what?"

I sat down at the table and drew a quick sketch of Gun Bluff. It was a method of communication, a kind of game we had developed in these last few days. It helped me put across ideas that might otherwise have to be repeated or spoken loudly. So I began, half talking and half sketching, to tell her about my plans for Gun Bluff. One of the sketches was of what I called my "Gateway to the sea," and Viola said, "Why that's beautiful, Evans!"

I didn't think. I just grabbed the sketch and wrote on it: "Would you like to go there with me?"

I pushed it in front of her and sat looking at her. She read it and looked at me. Her eyes were very wide in her face. "Wh-wh-why yes," she said. "Yes!"

And that's the way it happened.

I had just one more week in Abaco. Mostly it was spent meeting new cousins and making plans. The plans were that I would go back to Madison for my final year of teaching before retiring. I would sell my house there. Then in June I would come back to Abaco. Viola and I would be married and move to Gun Bluff.

It was sometime during this hectic week that I met a benign-looking white-haired gentleman named Dr. Stratton. He was a medical missionary and in the course of our conversation he remarked that he had once visited a few of the settlements on Crooked Island. "When you take Viola there," he said, "you'll be a long way from a doctor. You should get a license from the government and practice medicine there."

"But, Doctor," I said, "I'm not a doctor."

"Neither am I. Not an M.D."

"I beg your pardon?" I said.

He explained that in the out-islands qualified doctors are practically nonexistent. The Bahamian government therefore has adopted a policy of granting a limited license to persons having certain scientific educational qualifications. These are

91

known as Unqualified Medical Practitioners and may engage in general practice with the exception of major surgery. At that time all of them were ministers, endeavoring to serve both the spiritual and physical needs of their congregations.

The idea rather fascinated me. I had once considered being an optometrist and had actually spent the summers between 1927 and 1931 studying. I imagined that as an Unqualified Medical Practitioner on Crooked Island I would fit a few glasses, maybe bandage a cut toe and treat an occasional stomach-ache. It would be, I thought, an interesting avocation. It would give me a chance to know the people better. And I might even be of some service.

Anyway, when I reached Nassau on my way back to Madison I called on Dr. Fitzmaurice, the Chief Medical Officer, and made application. I told him of my Master's degree in biochemistry and of my training in optometry. He seemed favorably impressed and asked me to send him a transcript of my academic credentials.

I went back to Miss Taylor's to spend a few hours before catching the plane to the States. I was thinking of Viola. And the more I thought, the sillier it seemed to wait until next June to be married. I grabbed paper and ink and scrawled a hurried note: Why couldn't she come to Madison at Christmas? We could be married; then during the holidays she could consult ear specialists in Indianapolis. Viola had told me that her deafness had not "touched" her until she was seventeen. When she was eighteen she had gone to Miami to see a specialist. He had not been able to help her, and she'd had no expert care since then. Another doctor might be able to cure her completely. Medicine was always making new discoveries. There were excellent men in Indianapolis and she ought to consult them as soon as possible.

Besides, there just wasn't any sense in waiting until next June to be married.

I mailed the letter on my way to the airport. A few days after I got back to Madison there was a letter from Viola saying she agreed.

92

Sometime that autumn a doctor near Madison died and I bought his instruments and books for $45.00. I didn't examine them closely. I was too busy with other things: selling my house, moving into an apartment with my Aunt Mabel, who still lived with me, getting ready for Viola. But the books and instruments were cheap and I thought they might come in handy living on Crooked Island, whether or not I got my license.

On December 16 Viola was to reach Louisville where I would meet her with my car and drive her to Madison. The train was due about 4 o'clock and at 3 I was in the station. This was 1944, still wartime, and the place was jammed. Finally I pushed through the crowd to where I could see the bulletin board.

The train was eight hours late.

I waited. I walked around the block a few times, but I didn't dare go far. During a war nobody knows what trains are going to do. This one might not be as late as they said. And Viola was not accustomed to travel. Now she was traveling alone, during the holidays, in wartime when every train was a kind of drunken madhouse. I wanted to be there waiting for her when she stepped down.

The train arrived finally, at 1 A.M. People poured off, and I ran up and down the platform looking for Viola. I couldn't find her. Now people started crowding onto the train while others were still getting off. In the confusion it was impossible to see everybody. I made another dash the length of the platform. And no Viola.

It occurred to me that possibly she was still on the train. She was deaf; she might not have heard the conductor announce Louisville. Or if she heard him she might not have understood him. Nobody understands conductors. Maybe she was asleep.

I jammed my way onto the train and began to battle along the aisle, looking in every seat. If a woman was asleep with her face turned from me, I reached over and pulled her face around to look at it. There just wasn't time to waste.

93

I was in the middle of the second car when the train began to move. It was an express and the next stop was Chicago! And there was a solid mass of people between me and the end of the car. I started plowing my way through and over them. When I reached the platform the conductor was coming up the steps, the train already picking up speed. "Hey!" he said. "You can't—" I went over him and out the door.

But no sooner was I on the ground again than I was absolutely certain that Viola was still on the train. She was going to be carried to Chicago! She wouldn't even know where she was, an out-island girl alone in the middle of the night in a great, strange, wartime city. She would be sure I had deserted her.

But the train was gone, had rushed off into the darkness. There was nothing I could do except wire the Travelers Aid in Chicago to be on the lookout.

I started to run—and stopped. I backed up. And there, sitting bolt upright on a station bench, clutching a suitcase on either side of her, sat a very forlorn and lonely-looking Viola!

The wedding was set for December 23, the day after school closed. I had made no public announcement—in fact, Viola had been introduced as a friend of my aunt's who was visiting her for a few days—so neither the students nor the faculty knew anything about it. After all, I had been teaching here for twenty years and was known as a confirmed bachelor: I didn't want to throw the whole school into confusion just before the holidays.

So there were only a few close friends present, and the Reverend Bob Andry—the same Bob with whom I had almost starved on the beach at Long Island—down to officiate. Miss Drusilla Cravens, an old friend of my family, invited me to have the ceremony in her home. It was a beautiful place on a hilltop overlooking the Ohio River. Other friends furnished the music. Everything went off nicely, and by the time the story appeared in the newspapers, Viola and I were honeymooning in Indianapolis.

But the first day after school reopened in January the coach's wife stopped me in the hallway. "Evans," she said, scowling, "I have a crow to pick with you. You ruined my best tablecloth."

I could only stare at her. "I did?"

"You did. We were having dinner the night after your wedding announcement appeared in the paper when I told Ray about it. The news knocked the coffeecup right out of his hand."

We both began to laugh. "To tell you the truth," I said, "I think it was as much of a shock to me as it was to Ray. Even though I've had it planned since last summer."

Viola and I had taken advantage of our Christmas-vacation honeymoon to visit a number of ear specialists in Indianapolis and to try out a variety of hearing aids. The specialists were vague and the hearing aids didn't seem to work. Then in April Viola went to a doctor in New York. He told her the deafness was a result of nerve damage. There was no treatment or any type of hearing aid that would actually help.

So we had to face the facts and reconcile ourselves to them. But neither of us found them as disheartening as they might have seemed. Viola's deafness had never been much of a barrier between us. She could read my lips. And it was a kind of game sometimes to illustrate my thoughts with sketches. Between us we found no difficulty in communication. Certainly it was a handicap for Viola in her association with other persons. But we both felt that on Crooked Island, where everybody knew and understood one another, this would cause far less trouble than in a city. And so it would prove.

11

Viola and Piano Come to Gun Bluff

THAT spring of 1945 was my last one as a teacher. It was also a time of hectic preparation for the new life ahead. All kinds of things had to be bought or sold, crated for shipping or given away. But eventually the last box of dishes was packed, the last examination paper finally graded.

I left Madison High with very slight regret. I was not even worried—considering Crooked Island prices—about my financial future, even though I was a married man. My schoolteacher's pension amounted to $28.63 a month; but fortunately I had a little bit of capital and a very small income of my own. Also, I now owned more than a hundred acres on Crooked Island, having bought some additional land the previous summer. In the back of my mind was an idea of growing crops and raising cattle—a sort of misty picture of restoring the ancient days of the plantations. And maybe, I thought, something might come from the laboratory I hoped to set up. (The truth is, at this time I had almost forgotten my application for a medical license. When I thought about it at all, it was with the idea that the license, if granted, might give me an opportunity to know the natives better, to associate with them on a basis that otherwise would be difficult if not impossible; and that it might give me a chance to be of some small value to the island. But certainly I did not foresee it playing any important part in my future.)

Viola and I drove to Miami. We sold the car there and took a plane to Nassau. From Nassau Viola went back to Abaco for some of her personal belongings. I checked with Dr. Fitzmaurice, who told me my medical application had been approved but the license not yet issued. These things, it seemed, took a little time because of the red tape. So I caught the mailboat to Crooked Island and started getting ready for Viola, who was to arrive on the next boat, two weeks later.

This time I was going to take no chance on a mixup such as we'd had in the Louisville station. From the height of Gun Bluff the mailboat was always visible while still miles at sea, thus allowing me ample time to reach Landrail Point. Usually the boat hove in sight about 9 A.M., but by 7:30 that morning I was out scanning the horizon. Occasionally I would run back in the house to make some last-minute changes, then rush out again to look for the boat.

It didn't show up. Nine o'clock came and went. Ten. Eleven. At shortly after noon John McKinney climbed the path from the beach. "Papa Cottman, people is wonderin' why you ain' reach into Landrail Point yet."

"Is there any word about the mail?"

"The mail done reach long time. Mistress Cottman been waiting for you about two hour."

"It couldn't!" I said. "I've been looking—"

It couldn't, but it had. To this day I don't know how I missed seeing that boat. But when I did reach Landrail Point there was Viola, along with her dog Tripsie, both of them grown somewhat weary and short of patience. There was also, piled all over the beach and the sea rocks, a huge collection of assorted cargo. Everything we had shipped from Madison had arrived on the same boat with Viola and her things from Abaco. There were piles of furniture, crates, boxes, and trunks. There was a wind-charger tower, my piano, and half a dozen crates of Viola's chickens. Chickens, as I have said, were fairly plentiful on Crooked Island; but these chickens were Viola's pets and she brought them along just as she brought Tripsie.

97

I engaged every possible dinghy and most of the male population and we set out for Gun Bluff. It was too rough to try taking the piano that afternoon but we got everything else loaded and under way. As we rounded the north point the wind picked up and the water got choppy. It began to spray over the side of the dinghy. Viola's chickens got wet, then her suitcase got wet. In fact, by the time we arrived at Gun Bluff even her spirits were rather well dampened.

It was almost dark now. While I extracted a bedspring, mattress, and linen from the mass of assorted cargo, Viola inspected the kitchen. Her mother had given her a wood-burning stove as a wedding present but it was still crated. Now there was only the open fireplace in which to cook. She eyed it skeptically and went to work. Soon her skillet was black, her eyes were red, and her temper hotter than the skillet.

We ate supper, but only after Viola had stated, firmly, that the first thing to be done next morning was set up her stove.

Adjoining my kitchen I had built what Crooked Islanders call "a shade"—a thatched roof with open sides. Here I set up the stove. I drove nails into the wall above it for pots and pans to hang on. And Viola cooked breakfast in a better mood.

Now came the moving of the piano. For this I hired Frank Scavella's fourteen-foot dinghy, the *Grace*. I figured that any boat which could carry the cargo I had seen loaded on the *Grace* for that memorable trip to Acklins could certainly take a piano. And I was right. The weather was calm, so instead of trying to sail, the *Grace* was "tracked": one man walked along the beach towing the boat with a long rope while another sat in the stern steering to keep her from turning into the shore.

The big problem came when we reached Gun Bluff. I had brought eight men along, and it was a good thing. Out of old planks we built a kind of slide up the side of the bluff. Then we passed ropes around the crated piano. With four men pushing and four pulling we eventually got it to the top. There it was uncrated and carried triumphantly into the house.

All the men present had seen a piano, but some of them had

never heard one played. This was because there was only one other piano on Crooked Island and it had a somewhat tragic history. A young man had bought it as a wedding present for his bride, a very pretty mulatto girl who had been the belle of the island. In fact, some versions of the story claimed she had married him only because of the promise of the piano. The groom had had considerable trouble getting together enough money to buy the piano. Delivery had been slow—and before its arrival his bride had run away with another man. The deserted groom could not play. So the piano had remained silent.

Not so with mine. My workmen kept me playing for a solid two hours before they would depart.

Conditions at Gun Bluff during the next few days were hectic. I had brought a complete set of Haviland china which had belonged to my mother. It had been packed with care, and I carefully unpacked it. Not a piece was broken and I arranged it carefully on shelves built especially for the purpose. At this point one of Viola's hens came wandering into the house, apparently looking for a place to nest. She flew onto the shelf where I had just put the china, casually brushed off a teacup to make room for herself, and settled down to lay an egg.

If I had been able to get my hands on that hen she'd never have laid that egg or any other. But she went flying out of the door uttering alarmed noises; Viola rushed in to ask what I was doing to her chickens; and I made a mental note to round up all the chicken snakes on the island and try to domesticate them.

Viola on her part was having trouble with her stove. Under the shade it was exposed to the trade winds. Sometimes the fire burned too fiercely; sometimes it would not draw at all. So it was decided to build an addition to the barn, as yet standing completely empty, to house Viola's stove. We would then convert the rest of the barn into a combined dining room and bedroom. The big house contained our living room, the hurricane room, and my workshop. The hurricane room had a roof of shingles, but the others were thatched. In the living room the thatching leaked, always right over my piano. No matter where I moved the piano, it leaked. So I decided to close-board the living-room roof and cover it with roofing paper.

I gave John McKinney the contract for the new kitchen, to be constructed of the same tabby lime as the rest of the building. He soon had most of the walls up. My order of lumber and roofing was due on the next mailboat.

Unfortunately, a hurricane got there first.

There were no radios on Crooked Island and we did not know at first it was a hurricane. It was simply a morning of gray skies and gusty rain that got harder and harder. The view from the bluff was both beautiful and terrible: gray sky and gray rain and tremendous gray waves rising like mountains to have their crests slashed off and whipped into foam by the wind.

About 9 A.M. John McKinney arrived with a stranger, both soaking wet and moving bent over against the wind. When I let them in John said, "This is a hurricane comin' down, Papa. You best get ever'thing secure quick as possible."

His companion was the captain of the *Mayaguana Queen*, a sailing boat on her way from Nassau to Mayaguana. It had brought my lumber and was anchored now at Landrail Point. With this storm blowing it was impossible to reach Gun Bluff. The captain wanted to put my freight ashore at Landrail Point.

I told him to go ahead, then immediately got busy nailing down everything possible. Next Viola and I moved the Haviland china (that part of it unbroken by the chickens) into the hurricane room along with as many other small possessions as we could. The piano wouldn't pass through the door—and by now the rain poured through the living-room roof in fifty places.

The hurricane room adjoined the living room. Through a slot in the door I could see the roof of the living room bulge with the wind, see the rain drive through. I would rush in, heave and push the piano into a comparatively dry spot, and flee back to the hurricane room. Then the roof would bulge in

100

another spot; rain would sweep over the piano, and I would rush out to move it again.

When I was not working at the piano I could look through a crack and watch what was happening on the windward side of the house. The storm came in gusts. As they got stronger I could see the roof of my workshop lift and settle and lift again, rhythmically, as if it were breathing. In one gust the entire shade lifted, and kept lifting. Beneath it a fifty-five-gallon drum filled with rain water suddenly went over; then it and the shade together simply vanished. Behind them sat the stove, unmoved, with a light frying pan resting placidly on top.

This was my first hurricane, but Viola had seen a number of them. She was far less excited than I was. Until all at once she suddenly burst into tears. They flowed down her face like the rain down the front of my piano.

I thought of hysterics, of what I had read about the effect of a low barometer on certain persons. I put my arms around her. "Don't be frightened," I told her. "We are perfectly safe in this room. It will stand anything."

"Maybe it will," she sobbed. "But my poor chickens! They'll all drown if you don't go out and find them!"

There came a lull, and I went. I found one poor little black pullet, soaking wet and so weak it couldn't stand up. I brought it in. Viola wrapped it in a towel and held it near the lamp, meanwhile weeping for the rest of her lost flock.

Eventually, as they say, came the dawn and the end of the storm. In the first gray light I went out to inspect the damage. The shade was gone, but Viola's stove and the skillet were unhurt. The new addition to the barn was pretty well demolished. The roof, which had been only half finished, was gone and the newly laid walls crumbled. On the other hand, the barn itself was virtually undamaged. And from back of the barn came Viola's chickens, all of them, wet but healthy and hungry.

Shortly after sunup McKinney and a number of other persons from Landrail Point arrived, apparently happy to find we

101

hadn't blown into the ocean. The captain of the *Mayaguana Queen*, they told me, had not been so fortunate. On his return to Landrail Point the previous day he and his crew had gone aboard the boat, leaving their wives ashore. A tremendous gust of wind snapped the anchor rope. The wind was offshore and it drove the boat out to sea, leaving the four wives standing ashore screaming. The last seen of them, the crew had been trying to get up a sail. This had instantly torn loose. The *Mayaguana Queen* disappeared into the gray murk of sea and rain.

A few days later we learned the end of that story. The *Queen* had been blown across the Crooked Island Passage and onto a reef near Long Island. There it broke into bits. By something close to a miracle the entire crew had made it ashore safely. But not so the cargo, including my lumber. It was a total loss, and there was no insurance.

12

The Magic Sounding Rod

THAT fall, with the hurricane season over, Viola went back to Abaco for a visit with her mother. It was while she was gone that my license as "an Unqualified Practitioner" finally shuffled off its coil of red tape and reached me.

Quite honestly, it had been so long in coming that I thought little about it at the time. I was busy at Gun Bluff. I was trying to start a farm. I told Harry McKinney at the post office and John McKinney, working with me at Gun Bluff, that I had the license. Then I pretty well forgot it, for a couple of days.

Most doctors start out by studying medicine. Then they be-

102

come interns. Gradually they acquire a practice, and after years of this, if they are both lucky and good, they may become famous. My own medical career was somewhat reversed. I was famous overnight. Immediately I had more practice than I could possibly take care of. I never did go to medical college and my studying was done by lamplight and between patients. My internship, if it can be called that, came many months later.

It started this way.

Two days after I had told the McKinneys about my license a man came to Gun Bluff one afternoon to ask if what he had heard about me being a doctor was true. I started to explain, but he wasn't interested in the details. His seventeen-year-old daughter had spilled hot tar on her arm and burned it badly. Would I come look at it?

He lived at Cripple Hill, a small settlement about eight miles away, and I told him to sit down and rest while I got together the things I would need. The first thing I got was my text on burns. I read it swiftly, but carefully. It called for butesin picrate and penicillin ointment, neither of which I had. But I did have sulfathiazole powder and some vitamin-C tablets.

We walked the beach, barefooted, climbing over coral rocks now and then, and reached the girl's home late in the afternoon. Her burn was painful but not too serious; it extended from her elbow to the wrist and the tar was still on it. I set out to remove the tar with kerosene and absorbent cotton, working as carefully, as gently, as I possibly could. It took me two hours to get the tar off. Then I sprinkled sulfathiazole powder on the wound, bandaged it, and sat back wearily. I had done a pretty good job, I thought, and I was rather proud of it.

But in a few moments I was aware of an air of expectant uncertainty in the room. The father, the mother, and the patient herself, all were looking at me as if I had failed them in some basic, elemental way. I began to feel irritated. Had they expected me to cure the burn instantly? What did they think I was, a witch doctor?

103

"Doctuh," the man said finally, "ain' you gonna sound her?"

"Do what?"

He just looked at me.

"Sound her?" I said.

At that moment, though I did not know it, my future reputation on Crooked Island hung in the balance. I had no idea what the man was talking about. But then he glanced down at my bag, across which my stethoscope lay visible. "Ain' you gonna sound her?" he said again. "See if her blood is running right?"

"Oh!" I said. "Sound! Oh—sure. Of course." So I put on the stethoscope and listened to the girl's heart beat for a few moments and took it off. "She's going to be all right," I said. "She's going to be fine."

And now the place was all smiles. And I had learned a very important lesson not mentioned in any of the medical books I had bought: in the out-islands of the Bahamas the doctor's stethoscope, his "sounding rod," is credited with almost supernatural diagnostic powers. It must be used on every patient, no matter what his or her problem. No native puts faith in any medicine—or any doctor, for that matter—unless the wonderful sounding rod has been placed on him first. How else can any doctor know whether the blood runs right or wrong through the veins?

It was dark by the time I had learned this lesson, and I spent the night at Cripple Hill, sleeping on the floor of my patient's home. Next morning I dressed the arm again, left behind me a supply of vitamin C, sulfathiazole powder, and bandage, collected eight shillings for my journey and supplies, and headed back home along the beach.

I arrived to find that in some incredible way my fame had outrun me. John McKinney had already heard how I cured, almost instantly, a girl who was critically burned. Raphael addressed me as "Doctuh" instead of "Papa." In fact, from end to end of Crooked Island, it seemed the fragrant air had become instantly electrified with the news that a "wonderful

105

doctuh" was now living at Gun Bluff. Before the afternoon was over patients were arriving from Landrail Point. And first one then another would say, "Now, Doctuh, I know when you put your sounding rod on me, you'll know everything about me, and I want you should tell me the truth."

Any doctor might have been frightened by such blind faith. To me, with no formal training in medicine, it was terrifying. And it was that night I began in all seriousness my study of the medical books and journals I had brought with me. I literally burned the midnight oil. In my schooldays I had been a serious student; but never had I studied with such an urgent need as I felt now.

Nor was my studying all done at night. Many a patient sat placidly under my shade—the new one erected after the hurricane—while I searched my books for diagnosis and treatment. One man and his son arrived at Gun Bluff just at dusk, having walked from True Blue, thirty miles away. The boy was "given to fits." For a long while, the father said, the seizures had occurred only once every week or so; but now they were becoming both more frequent and violent.

I gave them pallets to sleep on, and I went to work. By 3 in the morning I had on my desk an outline for the examination, diagnosis, and treatment of epilepsy. I got a few hours' sleep and called the boy in. The diagnosis proved accurate. The newest and apparently best treatment I had found given in one of my journals called for dilatin sodium, a drug I did not have. I did have phenobarbital and I put him on that with certain supportive measures that were recommended. Then I wrote out for the father detailed directions on how to use the dilatin sodium when he got it, and I wrote to Nassau ordering a supply sent direct to him.

(Several months later I saw the father and he told me his son had had only one mild attack since beginning the treatment.)

Another of my early patients was a woman bleeding to death from internal hemorrhoids. I told her she must go to Nassau at once for treatment or an operation. She swore this was impossible and begged me to treat her. I was appalled. I told her frankly I was not qualified to undertake anything this serious. All right, she said, if I would do nothing for her, there was nothing she could do but stay on Crooked Island and die.

Reluctantly I agreed to try. Among my medical books was one called *The Injection Treatment of Hemorrhoids.* I read it three times from cover to cover. I made an outline of the whole procedure, step by step, memorized it, then pinned it to the wall in case I should forget. I did not have the proper type of syringe with a hand grip so I had to make one. With everything as ready as it would ever be I summoned the patient, said a silent prayer for both of us, and began the first treatment.

By the time of the third treatment I could see the first hemorrhoid was drying up. By the time the treatment was finished three of the hemorrhoids were gone and the rest were on the way out. Three months later I met the patient walking along the road carrying a huge bundle of firewood balanced on her head. "Doctuh," she said, "I do anything now. And all dis I owe you!"

I appreciated the compliment. It was several years later, in Marsh Harbour, that a doctor friend gave me another side of the picture. "You were just lucky," he said, "that you never had a slough."

"I know," I said. "I dreamed of that—had nightmares—all the time I was giving the treatment. On the other hand, I couldn't just let her die, let her bleed to death, and not even try to help."

At this time I was not only studying furiously between patients and learning the new language of the medical texts; I had also to learn the language of my patients. I had, I thought, become rather proficient in the Crooked Island dialect; but now I had to learn a technical side of it I had not encountered before. When a baby's mouth was sore because it had "de trash" I wondered what kind of trash it had swallowed—then learned that "de trash" was an inflammation of the mouth known elsewhere as thrush. One of my early patients, a woman, puzzled me by saying, "Dis mawnin', Doctuh, I cascade and

107

cascade." My mind leaped over a number of possibilities before I finally realized she meant vomit. When I asked another female patient about the general state of her health she answered, "Oh, I sees dot every month." And so I learned that in the Bahamas a woman's "health" was her menstrual period. Also, nobody suffered or was sick with anything; they plagued with it. To "plague wid de runnin'" was to suffer with diarrhea.

By far the most common plague was indigestion. In one form or another it plagued at least fifty percent of my patients. The reason is easy to understand. The average Bahamian working in the fields rises early, drinks a little tea, goes to his or her plot, works a little while, eats some dry bread for breakfast and again for lunch. In the evening the stomach is overloaded with a heavy meal of grits, cooked almost rock hard, along with some dried fish or perhaps conch made into a greasy stew. No fresh vegetables and few fruits. After years of such abuse the stomach naturally rebels.

I found that communication with my patients was generally easier if I spoke their dialect. So early in my practice I learned to ask, "You does plague wid gyahss?" And the answer was practically always, "Yes, Doctuh, I plagues plenty wid gyahss." I would then give a brief lecture on the value of a balanced diet, the need for vegetables and fruit. The patient would listen patiently; then, "Doctuh, you know we can't get none of dem things here. I want you should sound me and give me some medicine." This was all too true. So the sounding rod, psychologically, and antacid carbonates and belladonna became, perforce, my sheet anchor.

Toothache was a common complaint. There were no dentists outside of Nassau and the only relief I could give—the only relief these out-islanders knew to expect—was by extraction. I had forceps among my instruments, fortunately. One old man for whom I pulled a tooth began to shout, "Gimme dot teet', Doctuh! Give it to me!"

I wrapped it in tissue paper and asked jokingly if he was not too old to be putting a tooth under his pillow for the fairies

108

to exchange for a shilling. He didn't understand the reference. "Dot teet' been plaguin' me for two weeks," he told me. "Now I goin' to carry it home and build a big fire and put dot teet' in it. And when he start to holler, I goin' to start to laugh!"

I expect he did. He left Gun Bluff holding the tooth in his hand and chuckling softly.

As I had learned even before getting my license, there was in the islands a great need for glasses, "a spec" as the natives called them, always in the singular. Many wanted their spec so they could "see in de book" when they went to church; but one lady of sixty-odd refused to allow me to test her eyes. "I want you should give me one pretty white spec. So I could sport around in it and catch me a man."

I sold her a pair with plain glass in them and she went away happy. She must have been successful in her pursuit, for there soon developed a rush among the females of Crooked Island for the white spec with plain glass. In selling them I tried to remain ethically clear by explaining they were of no benefit to the eyesight. No one seemed to care. Apparently these ladies had already seen what they were looking for.

Those first few weeks of medical practice, with Viola gone and only Raphael to keep house, were hectic indeed. But after Viola's return things began to smooth out somewhat. That March (it was 1946) I even got around to installing the wind-charger plant I had brought from the States the previous spring. The government maintained an agricultural agent on Crooked Island, a Mr. John Rolle, and he had been taking a correspondence course in electricity. I had taught physics. Between us, and without either of us being killed, we got the tower erected, the batteries installed, the house and barn wired. And presto! Gun Bluff was ablaze with lights. I even installed an electrically operated vacuum pump for sucking blood and saliva out of my patients' mouths while extracting teeth. John McKinney had finished the addition, housing Viola's kitchen, and I converted my old tool room into an office.

The doctuh at Gun Bluff was in business.

And the patients came from miles around. By foot and by

boat, now and then a rare one on horseback, they came from the far reaches of Crooked Island, from Cripple Hill and True Blue, from Moss Town and Cabbage Hill. They even came from Acklins: from the settlements of Delectable and Hard Hill, from Snug Corner and Lovely Bay. And almost every one brought the story of sick persons back home who could not make the trip to Gun Bluff. When would the doctor reach to these points?

So I began to make trips such as the first one to True Blue, which I have already described. The roads were rough and rocky and I learned early the wisdom of traveling them the native way—barefoot. With shoes, the farther I walked the thinner my soles got; but barefoot, the farther I walked the thicker my soles got. However, I could never have carried with me the necessary supplies if it had not been for John McKinney's horse Shadow. Across his back I hung what on Crooked Island is called a chirone: a pair of huge saddlebags made of woven palm fronds and sewed together so that one hangs on one side and one on the other. These I filled with medical instruments, drugs, bedding, cooking utensils, food and water, until at times Shadow was almost hidden from view. He was sway-backed, docile, and completely faithful.

Along with the gear piled on Shadow's back I usually had at least one or two medical books. But far too often I would need books I had not brought. I would be confronted with cases where my knowledge and skill were inadequate. When I had applied for my medical license I had done so with no comprehension of the demands that would be made on me. Now, though I spent every possible moment studying, I was, at the same time, becoming more and more keenly aware of my lack of proper training. So in the summer of 1946 I wrote the hospital in Nassau requesting permission to come there for such training as would be helpful in my out-island work.

In September the permission was granted.

13

Dr. Maxwell-Joyner

Financing my stay in Nassau presented a problem. From the first my medical practice was busier than it was profitable. The natives of Crooked Island were poor, and I had adjusted my fees to the conditions. For a good hard month's work (and they were all hard) I would make on the average about fifteen pounds, or sixty dollars.

At Gun Bluff Viola and I could live on this, plus my income from the States. Living in Nassau, with no income from my medicine, was something else. So Viola went to Abaco to stay with her mother. Mr. H. A. McKinney (the McKinney from whom I had bought Gun Bluff) owned a one-room cottage about three miles from Nassau and told me I was welcome to use it. It was furnished with a table, one chair, and a lamp. I borrowed a canvas cot, got together a few essentials, and bought a bicycle for transportation.

So began my "internship."

From the first my position at the hospital was distinctly irregular. I was not an M.D. I was not an orderly. I was not an intern in the accepted sense of the word. Nor was I just a casual visitor. Nobody knew what to do with me; and quite truthfully, nobody cared. I was permitted, unrestricted, the run of the hospital: the wards, the operating room, the laboratories, observing what I could—and ignored. If I went into the operating theater I would scrub my hands, a nurse would hold up a sterile gown for me to slip on, then turn away about her own business. I would stand there, doing nothing, saying

111

nothing, and never spoken to. If I was looked at, it was askance, with a what-right-has-this-intruding-fool-got-here? expression.

It began to get on my nerves. Perhaps it was intended to. But after a week of this silent treatment I was fairly well convinced I would learn more from books and journals than from wandering, aimless and unwanted, around the hospital. Consequently I began to spend most of my time in the library.

I was there one day when a pleasant-looking, middle-aged man with a pronounced Scottish accent entered the room and asked for an eye chart. He got it and was about to leave when he noticed me. "Hello," he said, and came over to shake hands. "I believe you're new here. So am I."

I knew who he was. Dr. Maxwell-Joyner had arrived at the hospital about the same time I had; but unlike me, he was a highly qualified general surgeon and an orthopedic specialist. We chatted a moment, and just so there would be no mistake I told him quickly I was not a doctor but an "Unqualified Practitioner."

"What's that?" he asked and his expression was interested but not outraged.

So I began to tell him about my work on Crooked Island. After a moment he put his chart on the table and sat down to listen. Whenever I stopped talking he asked questions to get me started again. He was obviously, genuinely interested.

"And now you've come here to study?" he asked.

I said yes and added, perhaps a little bitterly, that I was having considerable trouble. He laughed. "I wouldn't doubt it." He picked up his chart. "I have to go now. But why don't you come out to my house tonight for a visit? I'd like to hear more about your work. And perhaps I can help you a bit around here."

So it was that Dr. Maxwell-Joyner took me under his wing and in all hospital matters made me his unofficial assistant. He was not only a warm and friendly man and an excellent surgeon; he was a natural-born teacher, gifted with that rare ability to impart information in such a way it can be both

112

quickly assimilated and long remembered. One job he gave me was to write up the case records of his patients; then he would send me to the library to study any obscure points connected with them. Whenever he went into the operating room, I went with him. I was given a thorough schooling in the techniques of surgery, how to ligate bleeding arteries, where and how to cut, how to suture. On fracture cases he was a near-wizard and he took great pains to teach me how to reduce a fracture and how to apply plaster casts.

Many of the post-mortem examinations at the hospital were made by Dr. Maxwell-Joyner and each one brought forth, for my benefit, a brief lecture on some phase of anatomy or pathology. I still remember the thrill I got from making my own first post-mortem diagnosis. Maxwell-Joyner gave me only the hospital record which outlined the deceased patient's illness, then told me to take over the examination. I suspected the heart, and with the doctor watching quietly, saying nothing, I opened the chest, took out the heart, and began to run a probe through the coronary artery. It met an obstruction and would not pass. "Coronary occlusion," I said.

Dr. Maxwell-Joyner clapped me on the back. "Good! Splendid!" he cried. "A strictly professional job!" It was obvious that he was sincerely delighted with my progress, and standing over the cadaver he gave one of his concise lectures on the pathology of the heart, discussing the causes, symptoms, and results of a stricture of the coronary artery.

"Now," he said, "I've got to run. You take over and finish up here." But at the door he paused. "Any time you decide to go back to the States to medical school, Cottman, I think you'd find it easy to get through. You have a solid scientific background. And you have natural ability."

He went out, leaving me feeling like a small boy who has unexpectedly drawn praise from the president of his country.

Inwardly beaming, I began to sew up the cadaver. It had helped me earn Maxwell-Joyner's praise and I worked on it with loving care. As I was completing the last stitches the door opened and an old colored woman entered. She glanced at the

113

body, then stopped. She walked all the way around it, looking at it intently.

"Doctuh," she said, "I been workin' round dis hospital twenty years. And I ain' never seen nobody could sew up a corpse as pretty as dot."

"Thank you," I said. "Thank you very much." It was truly the red-letter day of my internship.

The low occurred a few weeks later.

I had planned to spend Christmas in Marsh Harbour with Viola and had booked passage on the mailboat, leaving Christmas Eve. But when I went to go aboard there was only one crewman present and he told me the boat would not sail. "But why?" I demanded. "When is it going to sail?"

"Next week."

"You mean it's just going to skip this trip? Why?"

Well, it seemed the captain's wife had decided she wanted to spend Christmas this year in Nassau and the captain had decided he wanted to stay with her. To the crewman this was a completely logical explanation, and by now I knew enough of the vagaries of Bahamian travel to understand the futility of argument.

So I decided to eat my Christmas dinner at the hospital. There was to be a big party for the sick children; the governor and his wife were to be guests of honor. Everything was spruced up for the banquet.

Just as it was about to begin an ambulance came screaming in. Dr. Maxwell-Joyner was called to the emergency room and I went with him. It was a four-year-old boy who had been hit by an automobile. One leg was gashed from hip to knee, one arm broken and crushed, several ribs were broken, and there were serious internal injuries. For two hours we worked desperately. Now and then when a door swung open we could hear the laughter and songs of the other children. But in the operating room both of us suspected from the first it was hopeless. When it was over we stood there beside the body, not looking at one another, not looking at anything. Dr. Maxwell-

114

Joyner made a small gesture of resignation, palms up. He turned away and began to clean up.

The children's party was over when we came out. The governor and his lady were gone. The hospital dining room was closed. Dr. Maxwell-Joyner left to go home to his family. I got on my bicycle and went to look for a restaurant.

They were all closed for Christmas. At least every one in that part of town was closed and I had no desire or finances to investigate the big tourist hotels. I peddled out to my cottage, but the only thing in the house was a half loaf of stale bread. I took that in one hand and a glass of water in the other and I sat in my single rocking chair and ate my 1946 Christmas dinner, the worst and loneliest I have ever experienced.

14

Acklins Island

EARLY in January 1947 Dr. Maxwell-Joyner left Nassau to accept a position in the United States. Under his tutelage I had learned a great deal. I was deeply appreciative of the opportunity to work at the hospital with him. In February Viola rejoined me and we went back to Crooked Island.

Once more the patients, who had had no doctor during the five months of my absence, poured in. They came "to get sound" and to complain of being plagued with gas, with headaches, shoulder aches, rheumatism, abscessed teeth, and miscellaneous disorders that ran the gamut from the last stages of tuberculosis to the request for "nature pills" or sex stimulants. As before, they came from the far reaches of Crooked Island, from Long Cay, Major's Cay, French Cay, and Acklins. Each one brought the story of persons at home who could not visit Gun Bluff but wanted me to visit their home settlement. So once more Shadow and I started our long walks back and forth across Crooked Island. And finally, in answer to several urgent appeals, I left for Pompey Bay on Acklins.

I expected to be gone five days and I wanted Viola to go with me. But she was busy at Gun Bluff. She had brought back two more of her dogs from Marsh Harbour. Viola loved practically all "creatures," an Abaco term that includes dogs, cats, chickens, and practically everything but human beings. The term also includes insects such as mosquitoes and sand flies, but at this point Viola drew the line. Even so, she would be quite safe, she said, with her creatures for company and protection. And I was to be gone only five days.

Of course, we both should have known better. The trip was another variation of the one to True Blue. Patients came not only from Pompey Bay, but from Spring Point, Indian Well, Binnacle Hill, and Delectable. (I love the Bahamian names!) After five days, as the crowd in the yard began to thin out, a man came to me from Snug Corner. His wife, he said, was very ill, and if I would go with him (it was a half day's trip by boat) he would bring me back whenever I wished.

It was impossible to refuse. His wife proved to be dying of tuberculosis and there was little I could do except try to make her as comfortable as possible. But before I could get away people were arriving from Mason's Bay, Point Field, and Hard Hill.

I had brought a fair supply of food but now it was giving out. The local store, however, could supply flour, baking powder, evaporated milk, lard, and syrup. So I began to eat pancakes and syrup—three times a day. I also began to understand what my patients meant by being plagued plenty wid gyahss.

I have often heard people say they can't remember names but they never forget a face. My own mind works the other way. I can remember names, dates, telephone numbers, even license plates. But not faces. So when a man came to me at Snug Corner and asked if I remembered him I could only

116

shake my head. On the other hand I knew that somewhere I had heard his voice: it was not only the "deep" Acklins Island accent; it was almost like a bullfrog croak. "What's your name?" I asked.

"Luther Bain. I used to be cap'n of de *Cheerful*."

I remembered him then, and I remembered the *Cheerful*. I would, in fact, never forget it. "What can I do for you?" I asked.

"It's my little girl, Doctuh. She been sick for two days now. I want you should come sound her."

He lived in Mason's Bay only about a mile down the coast. His daughter, he said, was complaining of her throat and mouth hurting. I expected an infection of some kind, packed my bag, and Captain Bain and I walked over.

The child was a bright, attractive five-year-old. When I asked where she hurt she rubbed her hand across her jaws and around the back of her neck. "All right," I said, "let's have a look. Open your mouth wide."

She tried. I could see the strain of her effort and the pain it caused. Yet her teeth parted by no more than half an inch. "You can't open your mouth any wider than that?"

She moved her head slowly and tears came in her eyes.

I suspected tetanus immediately; but that was no diagnosis to be made lightly. Because I had no serum. I had no means of treatment whatsoever. Yet the more I questioned her the more sure I became. All the symptoms were there: the locked jaws, the pain and stiffness in the back of the neck, the pulled-down muscles at the corners of the mouth. It had to be either tetanus or strychnine poisoning, and a few more questions eliminated strychnine. There was no way she could have got it, and the pain had been going on for several days now, gradually getting worse. I asked if she had cut her foot or had a wound of any kind lately, and Captain Bain told me that about two weeks before she'd got a jigger in her foot which he'd had to cut out with his pocket knife.

So there was no longer any doubt. And there was nothing, absolutely nothing, I could do to help. I called Captain Bain

117

outside and explained to him. The only chance of saving his daughter's life was to get her to the hospital in Nassau, and quickly.

His face had a stricken look. "Doctuh, I don't have the *Cheerful* no more. Even if I did, you know she ain' fast."

I knew. But there was a wireless station at Long Cay. A radio message from there to Nassau would bring a plane. "Can you get to Long Cay?" I asked.

"I get there," he said. "You write me a letter what to say."

I wrote a hurried note to the commissioner on Long Cay explaining the situation, asking that he contact the C.M.O. in Nassau and have a plane sent immediately. Captain Bain put the note in his pocket and I walked down to the bay with him.

His boat was nothing but a dinghy with a sail. Ahead of him lay a forty-mile journey across open sea and already—it was almost dark now—storm clouds were piling up in the south. Thunder had begun to rumble. No man should be asked to start out in that boat in the teeth of a coming storm. Yet a few hundred yards away his daughter lay dying, and her only hope was that someone take a message to the radio station on Long Cay.

"Captain," I said, "it might be best if you waited until that storm passes."

He looked toward it, and at me. "You say we got to get de message sent soon."

"Yes." I tried to explain to him: these things followed no set course; a delay of a few hours might be fatal; on the other hand, treatment if given within several days might be successful. There was no way to know.

"But tonight could make de difference?"

"Possibly. I don't know."

"Help me get de boat in de water, Doctuh."

I helped him. He climbed aboard and raised the sail. He did not look back.

I returned to the house where Mrs. Bain sat by the child's bed. We could hear the storm coming. There was the steadily increasing rumble of thunder, the quiver of sheet lightning,

118

the wind coming in gusts and pausing again. Darkness came. And shortly after that the storm struck. The lightning was no longer in sheets. It ripped the sky, the thunder crashing in the same instant. Rain came in a deluge. It made a thunder of its own, and mingled with it was the howl of the wind. I did not believe that any boat the size of Luther Bain's dinghy could survive in such a storm. On the other hand, I knew how he had handled the *Cheerful* in the terrible waters of the Crooked Island Passage.

Sometime after midnight the storm passed. The morning was clear and we waited, hoping, for a plane. Neighbors had come in to help Mrs. Bain. Others stood in the yard watching the sky. And the day passed and there was no plane.

Next morning, when there was still no plane, one of the neighbors volunteered to take his boat and go to Long Cay. But as I wrote out a second note there were cries from the shore. Captain Bain's dinghy was coming in sight.

A half hour later he was ashore. He had fought the storm, fought the headwinds that followed it, survived somehow, and had reached Long Cay about noon. He had delivered my message to the commissioner who had sent it immediately to the C.M.O. in Nassau. The plane should have been here by now.

But it wasn't. And all day we waited, watching the sky, and no plane. Something had gone wrong. Had the plane broken down? Did weather conditions up the islands make it impossible for a plane to get through?

We had no answer, but the child was growing steadily worse. Her fever was increasing, the pain increasing. I did what I could to relieve the pain, but that was all I could do. Never in my life have I felt as futile as I did sitting beside that little girl's bed, knowing what needed to be done, and helpless to do it.

Next morning there was still no plane. However, the mailboat did arrive. It had no radio, but it offered fairly quick passage to Long Cay. Hoping that whatever had gone wrong concerned the message itself and I might be able to correct that, I took the boat. There was a fair wind. In the late afternoon we arrived on the south side of Long Cay where once I had gone ashore so seasick I could hardly stand. Now I hurried across the island to the commissioner's home. And there I learned what had happened.

"I sent your message immediately," he told me. "But I made the mistake of signing my own name rather than yours. I did that because all requests for a government plane are supposed to come through the commissioner. In reply I got a telegram saying, 'Take child to nurse at Spring Point for examination.'"

He shook his head in exasperation. "I knew what had happened. The C.M.O. didn't know you had seen the child. He thought it was some layman's diagnosis. And like most Nassau officials, he probably has no idea of the distances and time involved in out-island travel. Even so, it wouldn't have been too bad; I'd have got another message back to him immediately. But our wireless chose that time to break down. The operator couldn't repair it. It was this morning before a ship with a wireless stopped here. When it did I went aboard and sent another message to the C.M.O. explaining the situation in full, and then he got off his plane in a hurry. So by now your little girl has been in the hospital for several hours."

I thanked him and radioed the hospital. The child was there and the doctors were fighting a nip-and-tuck battle to save her life. At that moment it looked like a losing fight.

But the story has a happy ending. It took me several days to find a passage back to Landrail Point and by then the child had begun to recover. And only recently I had a letter from Captain Bain. He wrote: "I often remember how you came at my call and did all you could to help her and see her go to the hospital. She recovered from her serious illness and came back home again. She is now grown and is still at school. I must thank you again very much, Doctor, and I have given God the thanks for sending you here at that time. Whenever I could get her photograph taken, I would surely send one to you."

I was very pleased to get that letter. In this business there are too many moments of bitter frustration, like the afternoon I stood with Dr. Maxwell-Joyner and watched the child die on the operating table while just beyond the doors other children were singing Christmas carols. But there are also moments of satisfaction.

To get back to that particular Acklins Island trip: it was supposed to have lasted five days; actually it was a little over three weeks before I got home again. I found Viola worrying herself sick and inquiring about me from everyone she saw. She'd heard that I'd left Pompey Bay but where I had gone from there she didn't know. Her imagination had taken over and pictured me sick and helpless, or lost at sea.

"If ever you go to Acklins again," she told me, "I am going with you."

It turned out to be a promise she would soon regret.

One of my former students, Theodore Winkel, came out to Gun Bluff that summer to spend his vacation. He wanted to see as much of the islands as he could, so I agreed to make another trip to Acklins. Viola, as she had promised, went along. She also kept a diary:

July 16, 1947. This clear sunshiny afternoon finds us— Winkel, Evans, and myself—aboard the *Royal Mail,* a very small Acklins Island sloop en route to Mason's Bay, Acklins Island. We have been intending to make this trip for over a week but the boat only arrived today. So after an hurried pack, we left Gun Bluff at 3:30 P.M. The sea is quite smooth and so far we are having a lovely chance. But I dread the thought of a night aboard this boat. She is so small and there is no skylight or ventilation for getting pure air. Imagine!

July 17. We passed through French Wells cut last night just after dark, shortly after which the *Royal Mail* ran aground. The tide was high and starting to ebb, and they said we would have to wait until 8 o'clock this morning to refloat. It seemed to me morning would never come, I was that miserable in that little cramped cabin. Sometimes I would jump up and go out on deck for a breath of pure air, only to be driven back by the heavy breeze and cold night air. Unfortunately I had on only a thin sport shirt. Several times the crew pulled the sail over the

121

cabin door. I almost screamed for I have a horror of being closed in. They were sleeping on deck and were doing this to keep the wind off themselves. Winkel, Evans, and I were jammed together on the floor in one little place about large enough for three pups to be comfortable. As the tide ebbed the boat leaned farther and farther on her side, making us roll down one on top of another.

Like every other night, there is a dawning. But as 8 o'clock drew near we were as far from being afloat as we were when we ran aground. The captain pushed, pried, tried every means under the sun, but still the *Royal Mail* wouldn't move an inch. Finally he decided to remove her ballast into the dinghy, then he, the boy, and Evans pushed and pried with all their might. One time Evans had sunk almost to his waist in the mud. We all laughed, and so did he. I was expecting him to be as the preacher said: "A little while you will see me, and in a little while you will see me no more!" So Evans put the oar under him and stood on it while he pushed. The oar broke under his weight, but he kept on pushing, and shortly afterward she started to move. We were all smiles.

During this long wait our dog, Horrible, jumped overboard and got her daily bath. Like me, she hates to go without it. Then we were under way with a good stiff headwind. I would not go below in that cabin but remained on deck and endured the salt spray, which would drench us at times, also the hot rays of the sun. I feel as if I cannot endure another night aboard this boat. This is my thirty-ninth birthday, and I am sure I shall never forget it.

July 18. We finally arrived about midnight last night.

This is a three-room house with a little outside kitchen. It is practically unfurnished, but I have my own stove, bedding, plates, pots, etc. Sleeping on a blanket on the floor isn't very comfortable, still it is better than that old sloop.

July 21. The view is beautiful, and it is also very cool. There are lots of coconut palms and a large cedar in this yard, and these add to the beauty and coolness of the place. Yet I would not care to live here permanently. When I leave Gun

Bluff I want to get closer to civilization, not farther away from it.

Winkel's feet have been terribly red and inflamed from the sun he got on the seventeenth and he has not been able to wear a shoe since he came. I was very painful for two days after we arrived, owing to the hard rubs I got, but I seem to be O.K. today. Evans appears to endure anything and enjoy it.

July 22. We are now at Pompey Bay. We had a nice trip across, but I have added to the sunburn which I already had. We are living in the rectory and I find it much more roomy than the place we had at Mason's Bay, but not quite so cool.

Food is becoming a problem. There seems to be little or nothing in the stores here. Most of the people live on fish and grits, and not the kind we cook at Abaco either—some old rotten dried fish or conch, with hard grits, cooked two to one. It's a puzzle to me how they keep going.

July 23. Up early to get breakfast out of the way before the patients arrived. Evans is now doctoring the sick and I am trying to decide what I shall have for lunch. I have a little chicken but have decided to keep that for tomorrow, and have some fish today. I hope to goodness we can buy some. Someone has promised to send some when the boats come in. . . .

Later. The fish did not come in time for dinner, so I had to have eggs, fried banana, and fruit—not so bad after all. The fish came in time for supper and we all enjoyed it.

July 25. I did not do any writing on the twenty-fourth but it was pretty much the same as the day before, with patients constantly coming and going. Toward evening the sloop came to carry us home. Our former captain could not come and sent a grumpy substitute named Forbes. The trip over was not so bad, for the wind was fair and we soon ran across. Unfortunately though, that stupid Forbes anchored the boat at the wrong place and with all Evans' persuasion, he wouldn't move her an inch. As a result, most of our things got terribly wet in the rough seas, bringing them ashore that long distance. I hurt my leg trying to get from the dinghy to the beach, and was lucky I did not break it. But the climax came when Forbes insisted that Evans pay him more than the other captain had agreed to bring him across for. Evans paid it, but simply blew up. Our house rent, together with traveling expenses, ate up all of Evans' small profits. Those people just try to suck the life out of you, but Evans will still doctor them for a few shillings. I tell him I would soak it on them too, but he maintains this would only succeed in punishing the wrong persons.

When I bathed tonight I found several green and purple spots over my hips—the result of hard usage. It will be some days yet before they disappear. In any case, I can say with certainty, there will never be any more trips to Acklins for me.

15

Abaco

VIOLA was lonely.

Even before the trip to Acklins she had begun to sell me on the delights of life on Abaco, her home island. There she had been related to a good part of the population; on Crooked Island we were the only white family within a radius of one hundred miles. True, she had her creatures—dogs, chickens, cats, even a collection of goats by now—but she missed the old life as part of a large and happy family.

After our somewhat discouraging trip to Acklins we returned to Crooked Island to find the sand flies worse than usual. Viola pointed out that on Abaco sand flies were never this bad. We were in a period of drought; I had to haul water from the well in the quarry for my young fruit trees, and even so a number of them were dying. Viola showed me the official statistics to prove that rainfall on Abaco was much heavier than on Crooked Island. With both patience and persistence she worked at molding the pattern of my thoughts to conform more nearly with her own. She drew a lovely picture of her childhood, spent in the peace and charm of her father's Abaco plantation. To be sure, the plantation had been abandoned for twenty years; but the land still belonged to her mother, and without a doubt Mama would be willing to sell it.

I was not an easy man to persuade. For me Crooked Island still held a kind of magic charm. I could still step out of my door on a moonlit night and be as moved by the awesome and wonderful beauty of the island as I had that first night on the walk to Blacksmith's Landing. There was a part of Crooked Island that had entered my bloodstream, become fused with my flesh—that was essentially a part of me.

I pointed out that Dr. Stratton, the medical missionary who had first interested me in getting a license, lived on Abaco and might resent my moving there. "Oh no," Viola said. "He's only there part of the time anyway. And desperately over-worked when he is."

We wrote Dr. Stratton, and he agreed with Viola. He urged me to come to Abaco.

I had nothing else to fall back on. "All right," I said. "For a few months."

We crated and boxed about half our household belongings, leaving the rest, including my piano, at Gun Bluff. After all, I expected to be back before long. We took with us Viola's creatures, including the goats and chickens, enclosed in home-made crates. In Nassau these had to be left on the wharf for several days while we waited for the mailboat, and each day I had to walk down from Miss Taylor's to feed them. The mail-boat was to sail on Friday afternoon, and one of the crew assured me the creatures would be safely aboard.

At the proper time Viola and I, with our three dogs, Tripsie, Horrible, and Booze, arrived to go aboard. To my dismay we found the chickens had been loaded on the mailboat, but the goats had not. The tide was ebbing, the captain was looking

125

harassed, stamping up and down and shouting last-minute orders. I asked him about the goats.

"We can't take them!" he yelled. "No place for them."

My first thought was of trying to explain this to Viola. We'd probably have to stay in Nassau until we could find another boat. "Please," I said, "we can't just—"

He ignored me, turning away. But it was at this point Viola stopped him. Perhaps he had shouted loudly enough for her to hear, or the situation may have been clear in itself. She stepped in front of him, looking him straight in the eye. "Captain," she said, "I have passage on this boat. I'm going on it. And my goats are going with me."

He stared at her, and she looked back at him. His mouth opened, but closed again without sound. He backed off a step —and at that point he caught sight of the dogs. "Those can't go either!" he cried.

"Captain—" Viola said.

It was at this impasse the mate interrupted. "We could put the goats on the top deck, Cap'n."

The captain turned on him with what I have always believed was more relief than anger. "All right!" he shouted. "Put 'em there. Put 'em anywhere. But if they fall off, don't blame me!"

He disappeared. The mate called for help and started to load the goats. Viola asked me, "What's our room number?"

"Four."

"Come on."

"Wait!" I said. The captain still hadn't agreed to the dogs. But Viola was not waiting. She led her dogs aboard, put them in room four, and locked the door. "Now," she said.

And so we sailed to Abaco with no more problems. We moved in with Viola's mother in the house where I had boarded so briefly three summers before. I found a vacant cottage I could rent for an office. My first case was a fourteen-year-old boy from Dundas Town, the colored settlement adjoining Marsh Harbour. He was very ill with pneumonia; I gave him sulfa-drug therapy and he started to improve immediately. So once more I was famous overnight among the colored resi-

126

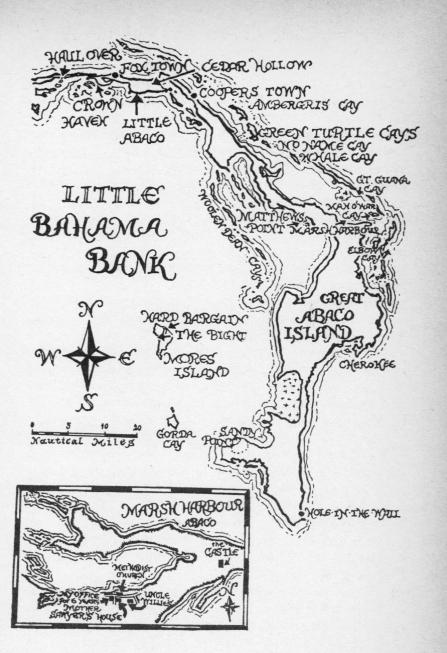

dents—not to mention the fact I was kin by marriage to fifty percent of the white ones. My practice was made.

Viola loved Marsh Harbour in the way I loved Crooked Island. She was happy here. I was busy with my work. But I was still troubled by my lack of formal training. I kept remembering how Dr. Maxwell-Joyner had encouraged me to try to enter a medical school in the States. There were a great many reasons I shouldn't, chief among them my age and the difficulty of living four to five years without pay.

Even so, I began to write letters to the deans of various medical schools. The answers I got were not encouraging. Some would take no students past thirty, and all were giving priority to ex-servicemen. My case seemed hopeless on both counts.

It was about this time, September of 1947, that a hurricane roared in out of the Atlantic.

We had several days' warning and the people of Marsh Harbour are old hands at hurricanes. Everything was thoroughly battened down. The houses on low ground were abandoned.

Mother Sawyer's house was not more than 150 feet from the bay so we moved up to the post office, already occupied by several other families. I carried a rocking chair for Mrs. Sawyer to sleep in and Viola carried a quilt. As usual I had to do things the romantic hard way: I took a machete and cut a pile of leafy branches to make myself a bed.

All night the storm howled. My leafy bower was not as comfortable as it looked and I slept little. In the morning, during a lull, Viola asked me to go back to the house and feed her creatures that had been left behind.

A good part of the road was ankle deep in water. The rain and wind came in gusts. Sometimes it was almost like being struck by a wave in the surf and I would have to bend far over to move. I enjoyed it.

Since the windows and doors had been boarded up, the house was dark inside. I lit a lamp and was greeted by Tripsie, but no Horrible. A search revealed her lying happily in the middle of Mother Sawyer's bed—nursing six puppies that had

128

just been born. Well, it was too late to do anything about that. I looked in our bedroom checking for leaks.

There were no leaks, but the bed looked exceedingly comfortable, after my night in the post office. Outside the storm was not howling now; just blowing steadily and the rain falling. I'll allow myself five minutes, I thought, blew out the lamp, and lay down.

The instant I awoke I knew I had been asleep a lot more than five minutes. There was a new sound from outside. It wasn't just rain beating against the house. There was the slosh-slosh of deep water. I stumbled across the room to a boarded window and peeped through a crack. The street outside was invisible; water was up to the porch floor.

Hurrying, I went out, renailed the back door, and started for the post office. The water was waist deep, swirling about me in all directions, carrying all kinds of floating debris. In one spot the road dipped; the water got shoulder deep and the current knocked me off my feet. But there were bushes all around me that I could catch hold of, and no waves. It was not really dangerous and the low barometer acted on me the way I suppose liquor affects some persons. I found it exhilarating, exciting; I had a wonderful time battling the storm and fighting my way back up the slope to the post office.

I arrived to find Viola nearly frantic with fear. While I had been having my beauty nap she had been imagining all sorts of things. Some of the other men had been sent to look for me. They had knocked on the door at Mother Sawyer's (I had been asleep, and there was the noise of the storm), then reported back that I had apparently vanished.

And I was lucky I woke when I did. All morning the storm increased in force. The eye passed in mid-afternoon, giving us a few minutes of dead calm before the wind struck again. Before it was over there were gusts, according to official reports, of 160 mph.

It was another day before we got home. Mother Sawyer's home had suffered little damage, but the cottage I had rented for an office was ruined, the floor, the walls and roof all torn and twisted. Even so, my medical supplies and equipment had come through almost intact. I found another house to rent and within a month things were running smoothly again.

It was at this time I got a letter from the dean of the Bowman Gray Medical School in North Carolina. It differed from the curt rejections I had become accustomed to receiving. In fact this man I did not even know had taken the time to analyze my situation more thoroughly than I myself had done.

He listed the problems that faced me: age and time and money. Then he asked: "If you should stop your work in the islands and take your M.D., what then? Would you want to return to the islands where you now practice? I have an idea that you would. An intense love of your work and of the country shows throughout your letter. And if you should return there, would the degree enable you to make more money than you do at present? Would not your fees have to remain more or less the same? Also, you would still be working under primitive conditions, without hospital facilities. Would it not still be necessary to send your more difficult patients to Nassau? At present you are doing a very satisfying and worthwhile work, a work of tremendous importance that you would have to stop for at least four years."

He then added: "If you still insist on trying it, I will do everything possible to get your application accepted."

I went over that letter a dozen times. Certainly it was right about my wanting to return to the out-islands even if I had the M.D. And it was true that without facilities I would still be limited in what I could do. And yet . . .

Truly I was at a crossroads of my life. And it was while I sat in my office, with the letter in my hand, thinking about it that Viola came in. "Evans," she said, "I am just about certain we are going to have an addition to our family."

For a moment I thought she meant Horrible again, though there was scarcely time for that. Then I looked at her face. And I knew she didn't mean Horrible.

I knew also that medical school was now definitely out of the question.

130

16

The Family Increases

ABACO ISLAND is about a hundred miles long and varies in width from a half mile to fifteen miles. Most of it is surrounded by a chain of tiny islands called the Abaco Cays, while the natives refer to Abaco itself as "the mainland." The waters between the mainland and the cays are comparatively shallow and called "white water" to distinguish them from the dark blue water of the outer ocean. The white water is usually deep enough to float craft with up to a seven-foot draft, and generally smooth enough for delightful sailing. There are scattered settlements both on the mainland and the cays; but roads, in the 1940's, were almost nonexistent; so all travel was by foot or by boat, and nearly all by boat.

I had not been at Marsh Harbour long before patients began to arrive from the outlying settlements, from Man-o'-War Cay, Hope Town, Green Turtle Cay, Guana Cay. And as at Gun Bluff they came with stories of sick persons back home who could not make the trip. So once more I began to travel, catching the mailboat sometimes, or a ride on a passing sailboat. (As in the Windward Islands, motorboats were very few and far between.) Sometimes I had to hire a boat, but my patients rarely paid enough for me to break even on such a trip. I bought a dinghy and learned to sail that on short trips, though I did not trust it or my own seamanship except under good conditions on the white water.

What I needed, I told myself, was a real boat, one with both

131

a motor and a sail, one I could count on to take me anywhere in the Bahamas. I consulted Viola's brother, Charles, who is an excellent carpenter. He in turn talked with Mr. Bunyan Key, an Abaco man steeped in generations of boat building, and the two of them agreed to build me a boat. She was to be a motor sailer, ketch rigged, twenty-four feet three inches on the keel, thirty-one feet over all, with an eleven-foot beam and three-foot-nine-inch draft. The cabin was to be divided into two rooms, the forward one for living quarters, the other for a little dispensary and doctor's office. My two builders worked out all the details of construction; my only ironclad specification was that there must be headroom in the cabin for me to stand upright. I foresaw long hours to be spent aboard that boat, many of them standing. And I remembered the low-roofed cabins that had tortured me in the past. I didn't want to develop a permanent hump in my back.

Meanwhile Viola went on a number of trips with me up and down the Abaco Cays, and enjoyed them much more than she had the journey to Acklins. She even went with me to Pine Ridge, a lumber-camp settlement on Grand Bahama Island over a hundred miles to the west. The lumber company there had no doctor and the officials welcomed us with open arms, giving us, rent free, a cottage to live in as long as we liked. They also furnished me free transportation on the only railroad in the Bahamas.

This was a narrow-gauge affair used for carrying logs from the forest to the mill. When I was called to one of the outlying settlements I would ride the "pumpcar," a sort of glorified Irish Mail powered by four men working hand pumps. It ran swiftly on level ground, fairly flew downhill, and had to be pushed uphill.

It was on one of these trips that an old man came to me to buy "a spec." He was nearsighted and I stood him close to the chart and asked him to read the top row of letters. He frowned and said nothing.

I moved him closer. "Now can you read them?" He squinted but did not answer.

132

It dawned on me that he might be trying to make a word out of F D T P O. "Just the letters, one at a time," I said. "The alphabet."

"Oh!" he said. Then slowly, "A B C D—"

His brother-in-law, who had come with him, interrupted. "Don't you know your letters?"

"Of course I knows dot," the old man said indignantly. "Dot what I saying."

I tried various lenses on him, asking him, "Now can you see that house? Can you see the window shutters? Can you see the boards on the shutters?" He could see them all. Not only that, with every lens I put in front of him he could see better than before. The first was good, the second better, the third still better, and when I tried the first again it was the best yet.

He had me baffled. I had no retinoscope with me and at first I couldn't figure how to get any accurate test. Finally I had him thread a needle using both eyes, then one eye, then the other. I measured the distance between his eyes and the needle and from this calculated the degree of myopia. It was a technique I have never seen in a textbook, but it is optically sound and since then I have used it a number of times.

I told the old fellow I would have to order his glasses from America and they would cost two pounds, five shillings. "I can't stand dot!" he cried. "I want a cheap glass."

He stamped out. I had spent almost an hour on him and I was glad to see him go. But in ten minutes he was back. "Here de money," he said. "Where de spec?"

I tried to explain again I had to order them from America; it would be a month or more before they arrived. "Oh no!" he said, grabbed his money, and left again.

Another ten minutes and he was back. "De spec come in one month?"

I told him it should. Somewhat unhappily he left me with the money and departed.

I have the end of this story only by hearsay, since I had left Pine Ridge before the glasses arrived. But they did arrive and the old man carefully unpacked them on the spot. Then he put them on and stood blinking for a moment. He turned in a circle, apparently to make sure they worked in all directions. "Well, praise God," he said softly. And then again, this time at the top of his lungs, "Well, praise God!"

At this point I was back in Marsh Harbour. The baby was due in mid-June and I told Viola I was writing to the hospital in Nassau to make reservations. This was while she was cooking dinner one day and she did not even turn away from the stove. "I'm going to have the baby here."

"But you can't," I said. "You shouldn't."

"I am."

I started to remonstrate. I was very calm and devastatingly logical. She was thirty-nine. This was her first child. It would be foolish, indeed dangerous, to have the child at home when we could easily make arrangements for the Nassau hospital. I had talked it over with Dr. Stratton and he agreed with me completely.

Viola went on with her cooking.

"So you agree?" I said. "I'll make the arrangements and—"

"No," Viola said. "I've thought it over, and I want to have the baby here."

"But—"

She looked at me. "Evans, I honestly would be much happier here. I'd be much more at ease here with all my family than in Nassau in a strange hospital with strange doctors. I'm not at ease with strangers."

"But—"

"Besides, my mother and her mother and her mother's mother and all my sisters and cousins have had their babies at home here in the out-islands. And I'm going to have mine here too."

That was it, temporarily. A few days later I had occasion to talk with the C.M.O. who had come from Nassau for a few hours' visit. He repeated, almost exactly, a phrase I had used to Viola. "It would be foolish and dangerous for her to have her delivery at home, Cottman. By all means, bring her to Nassau."

134

So I returned to the fray—and got nowhere. For generations Viola's family had had their children at home, and she was going to do the same.

It was June now. I stayed in Marsh Harbour, tending to the patients who came to me there but not venturing even as far as Hopetown or Man-o'-War Cay. I read, reread, and memorized everything I had on obstetrics—then read it all over again.

The labor pains began about 4 A.M. on June 15. Intermittently, they lasted all day and into the night. In the afternoon Dr. Stratton came to volunteer his help, for which I was extremely grateful, and at my request he stayed on. Viola was having a hard time and now it was too late to call a plane before daylight. The voice of the C.M.O., "foolish and dangerous," rang in my ears. I should have insisted, should have forced the issue, I should—

But it was too late to worry about what I should have done. The question was what to do now, right now. Finally I turned to Dr. Stratton. "What do you think, Doctor, about a pituitrin injection?"

I had never used pituitrin. I knew from my studies that used too early in labor it could be extremely dangerous. According to my texts Viola was far enough advanced, but the decision was still a serious one, a very serious one indeed, and God knows I was glad to have Dr. Stratton there to share the responsibility with me.

He was slow in answering, standing with his back half turned and looking out the window. His knowledge of the drug at that time, like mine, was based solely on reading. But here we were no longer dealing in theory. We were dealing with two human lives.

He turned to face me. "I believe we should try it."

It was then ten minutes before midnight. Less than five minutes later Faith Gayle Cottman was born.

Viola's recovery, I am sure, was more rapid than mine. And though I have since used pituitrin on several occasions in very difficult labors, and always with success, I have never used it without a tenseness in my throat.

135

17

I Was a Stranger, and
They Took Me In

With a new baby born and a new boat building, I began to think of expanding the range of my practice. At Marsh Harbour I was comfortably busy; but I kept remembering True Blue and the various settlements on Acklins, and how the natives in a settlement where there was no resident doctor would rush to one who did visit their area. Finally I got the idea of going to Andros, the biggest island in the Bahamas.

I wanted to go to Andros for the same reason I had first wanted to visit the Bahamas and then to go to Crooked Island and Acklins and Long Cay: because they held places I had never seen and people I had never met; a chance to be useful to my fellow man and, yes, a chance for adventure. When I did have to go to the States or even to Nassau I found the trip uninteresting. My hunger was for the small, unfrequented, out-of-the-way places. I have often tried to figure out why this is so and I believe it is because I can go to these unfrequented spots with an open mind, with only the slightest of preconceived notions as to what I am going to do and how I am going to feel. True, I make some plans; but they are loosely woven and pliable, ready for change and I enjoy having them changed. On the other hand, so much has been written about cities, I am inclined to go into even a new one with my mind pretty well made up that I'm not going to like it, and I usually don't.

136

Having decided to go, I called on Mr. Forsyth in Nassau. He had retired from his job as Andros commissioner, but was as trim and vigorous and enthusiastic as ever. He was delighted that I was going to Andros, telling me that although the Crown doctor (the official government doctor from Nassau) did manage to visit the island occasionally, it was much too seldom to look after the needs of the people. Together we spent several hours poring over a chart, making plans. I would go first to Mangrove Cay, practice there two weeks, then by catching the mailboat, which visited the island every other week, I could work the other settlements. In eight weeks I should be able to cover the entire island.

Mr. Forsyth once more offered me the loan of his house on Mangrove Cay, and this time I made use of it, moving in with twenty-five boxes of drugs, instruments, food, bedding, and a folding cot. I spent my first day unpacking and passing the word that a doctor done reach and would be available the next morning.

So bright and early I was ready for work, and there was the usual crowd in the yard. I opened the door and the first one who entered was a small, bandy-legged man with a sullen face and distinct odor of rum. "You is de Crown doctuh?" he asked. "You does give free medicine?"

I told him no, I was a private doctor and had to furnish my own drugs. Consequently I could not give them away. This he seemed to take as a personal insult. "I think you de Crown doctuh. I think you not tellin' de trut'."

I held onto my temper, repeated I was not the Crown doctor, and asked if he wanted to see me anyway. "You does draw teet'?" he asked.

"Yes."

"Whatya chyahge?"

"Four shillings, usually." (The cost of drugs and consequently my Crooked Island fee of two shillings had gone up since the end of the war.)

He looked outraged. "Cyant manage dot, Doctuh. One shilling."

137

I think it was the odor of the rum along with his general attitude: if a man could drink rum and get surly that early in the morning he could afford four shillings to have a tooth pulled. Novocaine, mouthwash, absorbent cotton, etc., would cost me a shilling, and more. Yet if I had believed he honestly could afford no more than a shilling I probably would have agreed—and what the result on Mangrove Cay might have been I can only guess. Anyway, I turned him out and called for the next patient.

This was a woman, and to my utter amazement she started on the same routine: "You is de Crown doctuh? You does give free medicine? I think you not tellin' the truth to us poor peoples on Andros Island."

She followed the first patient out the door with no medication, and another entered.

"You is de—" "I am not de Crown doctuh," we said, both speaking at the same time.

This one had a bursitis and eventually decided she wanted treatment anyway. She was one of the few that day who did. All morning the patients filed in and back out again, after a conversation that sounded as if it had been recorded ahead of time: "You is de Crown doctuh? You does give free medicine? You does draw teet'? Four shillings! Oh, Doctuh, cyant manage dot!"

All that day not more than half a dozen patients actually paid for medical service. Yet the next morning there was another crowd in the yard. I opened the door thinking maybe I had got rid of the dead beats.

I hadn't. The "patients" had simply found a new pitch. "Doctuh, I ain' eat nuttin' since day fo' yestiday. Please, Doctuh, you could give me a shilling for to buy a little flour or grits?"

"Where," I asked bitterly, "do you think my shillings come from? Certainly I don't get them from Mangrove Cay."

"Oh no, suh. You is pay by the gov'nor. You got plenty of money."

So there I was back to that idea, and nothing I could say

138

changed anybody. But I got fed up with persons smelling strongly of rum telling me they had not eaten in two or three days and were starving to death. Finally I said to one of them, "You were in here yesterday wanting free medicine."

"Yes, suh. You de Crown—"

"And today you want free food."

"I ain' had nuttin'—"

I pointed out the window. The house sat in a grove of coconut trees. There were hundreds of them on every side and most of them heavy with coconuts. "Why don't you knock down some of those? At least they'll keep you from starving."

He glared at me. "You one mean man. I goin' to report you." He flounced out.

And so it went all the second day. The third morning there was no crowd in the yard. There was nobody at all.

I didn't know what to think. I had encountered nothing like it before. On Crooked Island and Acklins the people were aware there was a Crown doctor, but they saw him so seldom, if at all, he was little more than a name. Also, from Crooked Island it was a two weeks' trip to the government hospital in Nassau and back, even if a boat was available. From Mangrove Cay to Nassau was an overnight sail. And as I was to learn, the closer to the seat of government the natives lived, the more dependent on the government and the less self-reliant they became.

Yet it was more than that—and this too I would learn later. The population of many of the islands, and in truth of many of the individual settlements, often has a distinct personality, sometimes in sharp contrast to that of an island or settlement only a few miles away. It is something I cannot explain. But I believe that anyone who has traveled extensively in the Bahamas will agree.

Anyway, now that the people of Mangrove Cay were convinced I gave away neither medicine nor shillings, the traffic to Mr. Forsyth's house stopped. Whole days passed when I did not see a single patient, and on an average day there were only one or two.

I did, however, have one particularly odoriferous case. She arrived one afternoon, escorted at arm's length by the constable, and such was her condition that I was aware of her approach even before I saw her.

Here I think it would be more politic to go back and explain what had happened than to give a concise picture of conditions as I first saw them. This explanation I got from the constable, who, as I have said, stood well away from his female prisoner.

A few days previous, the prisoner had engaged in a bitter quarrel with her husband over a piece of dried fish. Enlisting the aid of her sons, she had ambushed the old man when he was drunk and had beaten him nearly to death, thus landing herself in jail. On the afternoon that I made her acquaintance, the constable had escorted his prisoner from the jail to the outhouse. When she entered the floor collapsed, plunging her into the pit below. Obviously she had floundered there for some time before being rescued. Now she was wildly claiming all sorts of personal injuries and threatening to sue the British Empire from the constable right up to King George. The constable, thoroughly scared, had brought her to me to determine the extent of her injuries.

As he explained this, the woman started to sit down in one of Mr. Forsyth's upholstered chairs. With a wild cry I leaped to snatch it away. She staggered, and there was a horrible moment when I thought she was going to fall on the rug. But she recovered and I pled with the constable to take her away and give her a bath before I examined her.

He could see my point.

A little later they returned, a faint aroma of toilet water hovering delicately about the lady's person. After looking her over I told the constable, "A case of temporary stinkitis and a punctured ego. Nothing serious."

The constable looked perplexed; the lady was swift to take advantage. "You hear what de doctuh say! You hear all dem big disease I got!"

"But dot ain' serious," the constable argued. "I heah de

doctuh say so myself." He turned to me. "Ain' dat true, Doctuh?"

"I'll write a report and bring it to the jail."

He thanked me and departed. All the way down the path I could hear them arguing over the portents of my diagnosis. As they turned a corner out of sight I heard the lady cry, "Punctured! Dot's what I is! I goin' to sue—"

After this my life settled back into the routine of sitting on the porch swing waiting for patients who didn't come in. The mailboat that would rescue me was due on a Saturday. I would need all Friday to get packed, so Thursday would be my last day to see patients. Tuesday I wrote a note to this effect and posted it on a tree by the public road. That afternoon nobody came. Wednesday nobody came. But Thursday was the day the dam broke.

I awoke to a knocking on my door at sunrise. There must have been twenty persons in the yard, and more coming between the coconut palms. Now there were no questions about me being the Crown doctor. Nor, from their attitude, was there any indication that practically all of them had been here before seeking free service. I worked steadily until midnight and quit then because of sheer exhaustion.

Friday morning there was another crowd in the yard. I went out on the front porch and faced them. "I'm sorry," I said. "I am truly sorry, but I cannot attend to any patients today. I have been here for almost two weeks with nothing to do. Now I have to pack in order to sail tomorrow morning."

A flood of protests and excuses followed. I shook my head and went back in the house. I knew that if I gave in and started seeing patients that day I would never get packed. The mailboat would sail without me, and I would have another two idle weeks.

Yet I was unhappy in a way I had never been before in the Bahamas. It seemed to me that somehow the people of Mangrove Cay and I had failed each other. There had been a lack of understanding. Perhaps if I did stay on . . .

It was at this point I began, slowly, to pack my remaining

141

groceries. And discovered that most of them had been stolen, along with some of my clothing.

I decided that whatever lack of understanding existed between me and the people of Mangrove Cay, it would have to stay that way.

My next stop was the settlement of Long Bay Cays, south of Mangrove Cay. And here the Crown doctor routine was repeated almost verbatim. There was one added twist. Because so much of my food had been stolen I needed more and went to the local store. It had nothing but sugar, flour, and grits. I had no cooking facilities for flour, the grits were alive with weevils. I asked the price of the sugar. "One and six," the woman said.

That was at least double the normal price and I said so. She nodded agreeably. "You a white man. We charges you more."

"You can charge it," I said. "You won't collect it."

Across the street from the store was a house with a grapefruit tree in the yard. The owner was nearby, at her washtub. "Mawnin', mam," I said.

"Mawnin', suh."

"You does sell dis fruit?"

"Oh yes, suh."

"How much it is?"

"I charges de peoples here truppence. But you is de doctuh. You got plenty of money, so I is chargin' you a shilling."

Well, at least she was honest but I simply rebelled at being taken in this manner. I went back to my room in the little two-story building that served not only as jail and post office, but also as living quarters for any rare visitor who came that way. Here was the constable and I told him of my experience. "My my," he said. "The peoples is doin' you bad. You just leave this to me."

From my upstairs window I watched him enter the store. A moment later he came out, a package in his hand, and walked across the street to where the lady was washing clothes. And a few minutes later he was back in my room carrying a pound of sugar and four grapefruit. "I make the peoples think

I buyin' these for myself," he said with a huge grin. "So I only have to pay one shilling for the sugar and sixpence apiece for the fruit."

I knew, of course, he had bought them for half that. But at least it was a compromise. So I thanked him and paid.

From Long Bay Cays I walked to the settlement of High Rock, only a mile and a half south. And here, strangely, I found considerable work. The catechist of the local Catholic church allowed me to use the church office. Most of the patients immediately addressed me as "Father" and I was tempted to put on the priest's robe which hung on the wall.

At noon the catechist came to ring the church bell. When that was done he said, "Now, Doctuh, I want you should come to dinner with me. You have worked hard all morning; you have done much good for these poor peoples. So I have prepared a nice little dinner for you and I hope you will enjoy it."

I was delighted, for several reasons. First, I was hungry. But also I was happy to find a cordial person after all my troubles of these last three weeks. I was a stranger and ye took me in, I thought, moved possibly by the religious atmosphere in which I had been working.

The catechist's dinner consisted only of a plate of peas and rice, but it was sweetened with kind words. He was effusive in praise of the work I was doing for his people. He was sure that God had sent me here to carry out His will.

Then the meal was finished. The catechist pushed away his own plate and leaned back in his chair. "Now, Doctuh," he said, and cleared his throat. "Now, Doctuh, about the dinner. Ahem! About the dinner. What you say about one pound for the dinner?"

I could only gape at him. I thought I had been invited to dinner.

"Well, Doctuh, if you think that too high, how about sixteen shillings?"

I hadn't cleared that much in the previous week at Long Bay Cays. I told him so.

"All right, Doctuh." His entire attitude was that he wanted

143

desperately to do the right thing. He wanted to please. "I goin' to make this just as reasonable as I could. So I only goin' to charge you twelve shillings."

By this time I had caught my breath. "Look here," I said. "I thought you had invited me to dinner. That doesn't matter. But in Nassau I could go to a good restaurant, order a full dinner, and not pay more than six shillings."

The honeyed words and the reasonable attitude departed from the catechist. His lips curled in anger. "All right!" he shouted. "All right." He brought his fist down on the table with an oath. "Six shillings! But you something cheap!"

I paid him and walked out of the house. I was a stranger, I thought, and he took me in. He really took me in.

Most of my experiences on Andros followed the same pattern and there is no need to detail the rest of them. However, it would be unfair not to add that there were exceptions. One evening while I was at Long Bay Cays, torn between continued starvation and eating more of my sixpence grapefruit—I was getting sick of grapefruit at any price—there was a knock on my door. I opened it to find a tall, dark man, carrying a basket, and a light-skinned, very pretty woman. "My name's Smith," the man said. "Gordon Smith. This is my wife."

I suppose I looked at them suspiciously. By this time I was beginning to regard all Andros Island with suspicion. Anyway, Mrs. Smith started to grin. "Gordon is the schoolteacher at Driggs Hill," she said. "He heard you were having trouble getting food. So we brought you a small gift."

The basket contained fresh bread, butter, fruit, and canned goods. It was like manna from heaven. And certainly Mr. and Mrs. Smith proved to be some of the most charming and considerate people I have ever met anywhere.

Besides, on Andros Island there are settlements named Pure Gold and Love Hill. Places with such names just can't be all bad.

18

The Green Cross

I HAD left Marsh Harbour on September 17 and I returned November 24. This was two days less than ten weeks, and in that time I had cleared, above expenses, exactly twenty-four pounds, or a little less than ten dollars a week.

I got back to find Gayle growing lustily and my new boat afloat, but without a motor. I also found a long list of bills to be paid. So I went to work, and whenever I had a few spare moments I went down to watch the finishing touches being added to my boat.

There was a shade on the shore near the boat ways and usually there would be a half dozen men here, loafing and talking. The normal conversation at this time was about who I was going to hire for captain. I had already explained, many times, that I was not going to hire anybody. I was going to sail my boat myself. Nobody took this seriously. Most natives of Abaco have a built-in idea that they are born sailors, and an equally positive conviction that no one born elsewhere can possibly hope to learn to sail. "You alone?" they would say, looking at me and shaking their collective heads. "To sail that boat? You could never rule a boat that size."

"Could you?"

And the answer was always, "Of course. But I was born right here on Abaco. I understand these things. The thing for you to do is hire a local man. A good experienced seaman."

Day after day this went on. It was designed, I told myself,

to give me an inferiority complex, to destroy my morale. Consequently I became more than ever determined to sail the boat myself. I wasn't a moron. I had been able to get through school; I had been able to learn a certain amount of medicine; I had learned to live on Crooked Island. I could learn to sail a boat.

Yet the truth is, I was tortured by a deep, nagging doubt. From the boat-builder's shade I could see my boat, looking actually huge on the ways, or floating on the surface a few yards away. Beyond it, anchored in the bay there were generally three or four other boats, and now they had not only a romantic but a slightly frightening look. I remembered being desperately seasick on the *Lady May.* I remembered the cry, "De main sheet pop!" on the *Cheerful.* I thought about being alone when something of that sort happened. But I should have sense enough, I told myself, to keep out of storms. There was no need ever to be caught alone in a storm.

Most of the interior work on the boat had been done now. Charles was installing the motor. In a few days it would be ready for its maiden voyage. "You can't wait much longer," the men under the shade said. "Who are you going to get to sail her for you?"

I blew up. "All right," I said. "I'm a stupid American. I wasn't born on Abaco and suckled on a sailboat. But I can learn. And if I can't learn to sail her, I can sink her. Because that's what I'm going to do: sail her, sell her, or sink her myself!"

My answer was a pitying wagging of heads. On the other hand, I was rather proud of the speech. At least it put me on a limb from which there would be no crawling back. In fact, I considered naming the boat the S S S, for Sail, Sell, or Sink. But there was a popular patent medicine by that name, and since I was going to use the boat in my practice it didn't seem quite suitable.

A name for the boat had to be found, however. I was inclined toward some use of the word *Cross.* Not the *Red Cross,*

147

for that would falsely identify me as being sponsored by that worthy organization. Nor the *Blue Cross,* since that was an insurance company. There was a local boat called the *White Cross.* And the *Fiery Cross*—that would never do.

Then I was hit with the idea. The *Green Cross!* During the war, doctors in the States had been given a green-cross emblem for their automobiles to allow them to buy gasoline unrationed. So my boat would be the *Green Cross.* Viola had a picture of Columbus landing at San Salvador, right here in the Bahamas, and on the sail of the *Santa Maria* was painted a huge Maltese cross. So I copied the design and painted a large green Maltese cross on each bow of my boat.

And now there was nothing left but to sail her.

I went to Viola's uncle, Mr. Willie Roberts. He was a small, frail man in his seventies with gray hair and a gentle voice. Truly he had been born on Abaco and suckled on a sailboat; he knew as much about sailing as one man could know. But he had never been among those who claimed it was impossible for me, as an outsider, to have brains and skill enough to learn. "Uncle Willie," I said, "can you—will you—teach me to handle the *Green Cross?*"

"I'll be glad to, Evans. It shouldn't be any problem."

The boat was anchored out in the harbor. We sculled out in the dinghy and went aboard for the first lesson. For an hour Uncle Willie simply drilled me on names. Halyard, jib sheet, starboard, port. He wanted me to know what he was talking about when he used the terms. (I already knew what a tiller was, thanks to Percy Cavill's lesson of years before.) Then with Uncle Willie in control, telling me what to do, we began to hoist sails, sail a few moments, tack, lower sails, drop anchor, weigh anchor, hoist sails, jibe. On and on.

There were two long sessions of this. On the third trip Uncle Willie said, "This time I'm going to sit on the deck and watch. You handle the boat yourself."

"But—"

"I want you to take up the anchor, sail out of the harbor,

beat up against the wind for a while, then bring her back here and anchor her. Now I'm not going to say another word, unless you get into a jam."

I did it. When it was over Uncle Willie had suggestions but little criticism. Yet he wanted one more trip as a silent observer. After that he said, "Tomorrow you take her out alone."

There were half a dozen Cassandras sitting under the shade next day and shaking their heads as I sculled out to the *Green Cross*. It didn't help my confidence, but it made it impossible for me to turn back. Without Uncle Willie the *Green Cross* seemed three times as big as ever before. Now if something went wrong there was nothing to fall back on except my own feeble wits.

I hoisted my little spanker and trimmed the sheet in close. The boat headed into the wind just as she was supposed to do. I slacked the jib sheet and main sheet and hoisted the two big sails. They flapped idly in the breeze.

Now came the moment of truth. I went forward to the anchor. Once it was weighed I was at the mercy of wind, wave, and my own ability. Slowly I pulled in the hawser, laying it in neat coils as Uncle Willie had taught me to do, saying to myself: I want the boat to turn left—port. So I push the jib boom to the right—starboard. Then I—

The anchor broke the surface. Quickly I dropped it on the deck. I grabbed the boom and pushed it as far to starboard as I could. The wind caught the sail. The boat began to drift backward. She hovered, as if undecided. I let go the jib boom, ran aft, and trimmed the jib sheet and main sheet. The sails filled. The *Green Cross* moved forward and to the left, exactly as she was supposed to do!

I sailed out into the passage, tacked, and jibed, back and forth; I came back in the harbor. I anchored exactly where I had been, furled my sails and tied them, and sculled ashore. I walked up to the group sitting under the shade. Uncle Willie was with them. "Nice trip?" he said.

"Splendid," I said. "No trouble at all."

"I didn't think you would have," Uncle Willie said. "Given a little experience, you'll rule that boat as well as anybody around here could do."

The others, it seemed, did not hear him. They were talking about the weather. They kept right on talking about the weather. But I needed no word from them. Uncle Willie's praise and my own feeling of satisfaction were enough. In fact, I was so carried away that I announced, somewhat too casually, that I thought I'd sail over to Pine Ridge on Grand Bahama.

The talk about the weather ceased. There was a long moment of stunned silence. Even Uncle Willie's face had an expression of doubt. Then one of the men asked, "Who's going to sail the boat for you?"

"I'm going to sail it myself."

Immediately the chorus of Job's Comforters went into action.

"You can't do that. You'll run on a reef."

"You'll lose your boat."

"You'll be drowned."

"You don't even know the way."

"I believe I can read a chart," I said coldly.

One man replied, "The charts aren't always exact, Evans. The channels change sometimes."

"I'll ask someone who's been across recently," I said. "That's all anyone else could do."

Viola and Uncle Willie were the only ones who had any faith in me—and Viola's faith was somewhat shaken at the idea of my taking a hundred-mile cruise alone. Yet it was for trips of this kind I'd had the *Green Cross* built, and hiring a captain was financially out of the question. So one day I set sail for Pine Ridge, feeling somewhat like Columbus sailing toward the unknown edge of the world—except Columbus had a lot of other persons with him.

There was a good easterly breeze blowing and my course was northwest, in the comparatively calm white water between

150

the mainland of Abaco and the outlying rim of cays. For three hours everything was perfect; the sun was warm and the wind was good. My confidence grew. Before long I was reciting to myself from John Masefield's "Sea Fever":

> *Oh, I must go down to the seas again, for the call*
> *   of the running tide*
> *Is a wild call and a clear call that may not be denied;*
> *And all I ask is a windy day with the white clouds*
> *   flying,*
> *And the flung spray and the blown spume, and the sea*
> *   gulls crying.*

Just south of Whale Cay there is a long shallow bar open to the great ocean waves that come through the pass to the east. My course should have taken me well to the west where, according to Uncle Willie, I would find the Sandbank Cays channel. Yet somehow (it seemed to happen all at once) there was the bar directly in front of me with waves breaking across it in frothy fury. One moment I was bowling along singing; the next the world was filled with altogether too much flung spray and blown spume, and anything the sea gulls were crying I couldn't hear.

Swiftly I brought the *Green Cross* around, heading directly back into the wind. But there was no time now for tacking. I called on my ace in the hole, and pushed the starter button on the engine.

In training with Uncle Willie I had used the engine very little. It had been installed as a safety measure, to be used only in emergencies. And now was an emergency. The motor caught instantly. The *Green Cross* surged away from the bar—for about fifty feet. There, without warning, the motor quit.

Again I pushed the button. The battery ground, but the motor was silent. Now the *Green Cross* was drifting back toward the bar. Already I had lost the fifty feet I'd gained, and there wasn't much more to lose.

I ran forward and threw over the anchor. If it didn't hold— But it did. The *Green Cross* rose and fell with the surge of the

151

waves, her stern almost at the edge of the bar. Just how long the anchor would hold her there was another matter.

I dived below to examine the motor and came to the quick conclusion the fuel line was clogged with dirt. I disconnected the line, and no gas came through. There was no wire I could use to clear the line, so I put my mouth over the end and blew. I blew until my eyes bulged in their sockets—and finally heard the gas bubbling in the tank. That meant whatever had blocked the line had been blown back into the tank. At least for a while the line was clear.

When I took my mouth off the line, gas spouted out, over me and the engine. There was no shutoff valve at the tank. A stupid oversight, I thought; but there was no time now to worry about that. As hastily as possible I got the line screwed back to the motor and raced on deck.

My stern looked even closer to the breakers than it had before, if that was possible. I ran forward and checked the anchor line. It was holding, or it seemed to be. Maybe just my imagination. I got the sails down fast, said a prayer even faster, and pushed the starter. The motor caught. Now if it would just run for a while, for just a little while.

I tied the tiller in the center, throttled down, and threw in the clutch. The *Green Cross* moved slowly ahead. I leaped forward and began to haul on the anchor line, dropped it on deck, ran back to the tiller, and opened the throttle. The boat surged forward. It surged a good hundred yards, and the motor quit again.

It was all to do over, but at least the breakers were farther behind me. Under way once more, I turned south, looking for the Sandbank Cays channel Uncle Willie had told me about. But all I could see were breakers and sandbars. The whole sea had suddenly become composed of nothing else.

Then, just where Uncle Willie had said it was, I saw a greenish, twisting pathway. I headed into it. The motor purred smoothly. But the water was shallow. Twice the *Green Cross* tipped the sandy bottom. What about the tide? I had forgotten about that. It would be low now. And just to my left was a

152

rocky bank with the rotting wreck of a sailboat piled high on it. With one hand I rubbed my throat, trying to push my heart back down where it belonged.

Ahead the green path widened. The water was deep and calm all around. I had passed through the channel. "All right," I said aloud to the motor. "If you want to cut off now, it's all right with me."

Two hours later, at Green Turtle Cay, I found a mechanic to work on my gas line while I sent a telegram to Viola: "Safe at Green Turtle Cay. Fine trip. Proceeding to Pine Ridge. Love, Evans."

19

I Take a Job

A T Pine Ridge, which I reached after several more scares but no serious trouble, I found more work than I could take care of. However, I didn't stay long. I figured that now I was an old salt, an experienced Bahamian seaman, there was no reason I shouldn't have Viola and Gayle with me on my floating office. So I sailed back to Marsh Harbour, loaded my family aboard, and headed once more for Grand Bahama Island.

This time Cottman, the ancient mariner, did not get caught in the breakers at Whale Cay. I didn't have to search for the Sandbank Cays channel because I used another and better one just under the lee of Whale Cay. That night, our first family night aboard the *Green Cross*, we were cozily secure at Green Turtle Cay.

Next morning there was a twenty-five-knot wind blowing. It blew out of the southeast and we wanted to go northwest, and I had not yet learned caution. So we sailed, and it was glorious! The *Green Cross* fairly skimmed along. Cay after cay sped by. Once during the morning there was a sudden downpour of rain and Viola and Gayle took shelter in the cabin. But the weather was warm; I stood at the tiller not even bothering with a waterproof and watched the spray fly.

We had planned to reach Hawksbill Cay by evening; actually we were there a few minutes after noon. "Let's not stop now," I told Viola. "With this wind we can reach Sales Cay easily."

Viola had spent all her life around water. She demurred, but only slightly, and on we went.

There was another squall, and then another. The wind pulled into the south, then to the south-southwest. Big seas began to roll on us broadside. Gayle got seasick. I had to alter the course from northwest to west by south in order to round the point of Sales Cay. All this served to bring the wind more and more ahead until we could no longer fetch a course. I decided to lower the sails and start the motor.

The jib and mizzen came down easily, but the mainsail was laced to the mast and the rains had shrunk the lacing tight against the tall spar. I had no down-haul on the mainsail. I had asked one of the Marsh Harbour experts about a down-haul but he had merely looked at me patronizingly and said nobody put a down-haul on the mainsail. "The mainsail," he had told me, "is so heavy it falls of its own weight."

So it had—in dry weather. But not now. The only way now to get the sail down was to climb up and pull it down. My arms tight around the mast, toes gripping the lacing, I began to climb.

Viola was in the cabin with Gayle, so she did not see me. The *Green Cross*, broadside to the waves, began to roll, more and more violently. The mast whipped back and forth. One moment I was hanging far out over the water on the starboard side, the next moment far out to port. I had a vision of what would happen if I fell in that sea. The *Green Cross* was drifting with the wind. Viola might not be able to hear my cries. . . .

154

I heard her cry all right: one loud, anguished, terrible wail. At that moment the lacing began to yield; the sail suddenly slid gracefully down and I came crashing, less gracefully, after it. In the same instant Viola's cry stopped and I jumped for the cabin door. There was a table bolted to the floor in the middle of the cabin with bunks on each side. Viola had been washing dishes here and, as well as possible, taking care of Gayle at the same time. Apparently she had turned away from the dishpan for a moment; in that moment the boat had rolled more violently than before, and the water and dishes had spilled onto the nearby bunk and baby. Viola's cry had come in the instant she grabbed for, and missed, the dishpan. Now it was Gayle's turn.

Her screams, however, were from indignation rather than injury. I went back on deck and got the motor going. At exactly 5 P.M. we dropped anchor in the calm water off the southwest point of Sales Cay. We had covered sixty-two miles in ten hours, and since the last part of the trip had been slow, I estimated we had averaged better than eight knots during the first six hours.

Next day, with less speed and less excitement, we went south to Hawksbill Creek on Grand Bahama Island. This creek, a few miles west of Pine Ridge, cuts the island in two. On the north side it was wide and navigable for several miles. Then it narrowed and became so shallow only a dinghy could get through.

All this is now changed. Huge dredging operations have enlarged the south entrance into a great artificial harbor. A free port, one of the seven in the world, has been established here. There are cement and fertilizer factories, bunkers for refueling ocean-going ships, and—of all things—a medical research center. Only a few miles away at West End there is now a big tourist hotel with air-conditioned rooms, a golf course and tennis courts, an anchorage for private yachts as well as for the guide boats that work the nearby Gulf Stream for marlin, sailfish, and tuna.

Things were somewhat different in February 1949. There

155

were only two tiny settlements near the south end of Hawksbill Creek: Eight Mile Rock on the west and Pinder Point on the east. I took the *Green Cross* as far as possible into the creek and anchored, at a point about three miles from both settlements. Soon the word got around: "A doctuh done reach Hawksbill Creek," and streams of people began to arrive in dinghies from both settlements.

We stayed here a week. Then I put Gayle and Viola in our dinghy and sculled down to Pinder Point. Here Dr. Stratton had built a beautiful but tiny hospital in connection with his missionary work. It was open only on the occasions of his rare visits, and before leaving Marsh Harbour I had asked permission to use it. It was of white concrete with an arched roof, built on a bluff overlooking the ocean. Here Viola set up housekeeping and I set up shop. And the patients poured in. For a week I worked every day from shortly after dawn until well after dark.

With most of the people of Pinder Point and Eight Mile Rock well sounded, we went back to Pine Ridge. And here, even before I had a chance to go ashore, I was greeted by two officials of the lumber company who came out in a motorboat to meet me. They had a proposition.

The nurse who had been with them for several years had quit and gone to Nassau, leaving the company with no medical services whatsoever. Whenever an employee got sick or injured—and there were a lot of injuries—a plane had to be chartered to fly him to Nassau. The company had hired a doctor, a German who had fled Hitler's regime several years earlier and gone to England. But he was still involved in the red tape of immigration and it would be at least two months before he arrived. In the meanwhile, would I take the job?

I talked it over with Viola. She had left her creatures and her mother at home and did not feel she could stay away another two months. On my part, I was in love with the *Green Cross*, and wanted to keep sailing her to new ports—wherever I was needed and as far as I could go. Unfortunately, however, there was the immediate matter of money to be considered. I

156

was broke. The fee the company named was a good one; the work was only three days a week and I was free to treat private patients the rest of the time. The *Green Cross* and the new ports would still be there after two months. Once a week there was a plane from Pine Ridge to Marsh Harbour, and Viola and Gayle could take it when Viola felt they must go home.

I told the lumber company officials they had just hired a doctor.

It turned out to be a very busy two months. The private patients were, as usual, plagued with gas and "wombs troubles," a term that covered everything from tumors to gonorrhea. The company patients were an endless series of cuts, bruises, burns, and breaks. Time and again I gave thanks to Dr. Maxwell-Joyner for the training he had given me in handling fractures.

There were two days that I particularly remember.

One was a day while Viola and Gayle were still with me. A nor'wester was making up, the wind getting stronger all morning. By early afternoon it was blowing a gale. The *Green Cross* was pitching crazily, and though I was anchored only two hundred feet from the dock, it was a dangerous two hundred feet. Naturally this was the afternoon to welcome a flood of private patients. They stood on the dock and shouted for me to come get them.

My dinghy was tied to the stern. Putting the outboard motor on it was like (or so I would imagine) putting a saddle on a wild steer. But eventually I got it fastened, fought the seas, and arrived at the dock.

Immediately the whole crowd started to climb down and get into the boat at one time, the women and children last because the men managed to push ahead. "Stop!" I shouted. "You'll sink the boat! I can't take but four at a time!"

Nobody paid any attention. There were already six in the dinghy, sinking it almost to the gunwales. I pushed violently away from the dock, leaving another half dozen dangling and the whole crowd screaming for me to take them too.

Somehow we made it back to the *Green Cross,* all of us

157

soaking wet. I treated them, pulled a tooth—tricky work in a pitching boat—then we climbed in the dinghy again. With the wind driving us we raced for the dock.

This time there was utter confusion. Some were getting out while others were climbing over them to get in. In a minute the dinghy was jammed and so low in the water that we'd have sunk right there if we hadn't been in the lee of the dock. I pointed to the three men nearest me. "You'll have to get out and wait for the next trip."

They refused. They had fought their way into the dinghy and they meant to stay. There was no point in arguing with them. So I picked up the end of the bowline, climbed on the dock, and sat down. "Now," I said, "you can stay there all afternoon if you want. But I am not going to take an overloaded boat in that water and drown these women and babies."

There was a moment of heavy silence. Then one of the women said, "You hear what de doctuh say. Why don't you act wid some sense?"

Another addressed one of the men, apparently her husband. "Get out de boat. You make me shame."

There was some grumbling, but the men yielded. Again we made it to the *Green Cross* through heavy spray. But this time when we were ready to return, the outboard motor refused to start. There was nothing to do but take the oar and try to scull.

At this time I was no expert in sculling, and even if I had been I couldn't have kept a straight course in that wind. We headed not for the dock, but for a point on the beach some two hundred yards from it. As we approached the surf got higher. The women began to scream. The men on the dock were yelling useless advice. I knew that if a wave caught us broadside we would turn over. So I did the only thing I could. As the water got shallow I jumped overboard, grabbed the bow of the dinghy, and towed it to the dock.

Fortunately the lumber company kept a motorboat alongside the dock. Two men offered to tow me and the dinghy and the remaining patients to the *Green Cross*.

When it was all over and the last patient gone, I went be-

158

low. Gayle lay kicking and squirming on one of the bunks. Viola stood between her and the little Primus stove. With one hand she was trying to keep Gayle from either crawling off or being rolled off the bunk; with the other hand she was trying to keep the little portable oven from falling off the stove. And she was having trouble with both. "This bread is going to be a failure," she moaned. "I know it. And I've been working at it all afternoon."

"It smells delicious."

"The oven kept falling off—" She gestured at a Rube Goldberg contraption of wires she had rigged up to hold it in place. "Even after—" She stopped, looking at my soaked clothing. "What happened, Evans?"

I explained my difficulties of the afternoon. She explained the contraption she had invented to hold the oven. And together we ate the bread. She had never made better.

The other day I particularly remember from that time at Pine Ridge was after Gayle and Viola had returned home. On this morning I awoke with a raw throat and a temperature. If I had been a patient, I would have put myself to bed for the day. But I had promised a woman patient to remove a benign tumor from her back, the operation to be done in her home. So I forced myself to eat a bite of breakfast, sculled the dinghy ashore, and went to the clinic to get my materials and instruments.

Before I could leave a man with a broken foot was brought in. By the time I finished putting that in a cast it was 11 o'clock. I had been scheduled to do the operation at 9.

At the woman's house I sterilized my hands, anesthetized the area around a broad, low, rather ill-defined lump on her back, and made a four-inch incision. I encountered only muscle, though I could still plainly feel the lump. I introduced a retractor, found the edge of the muscle, drew it aside, and turned the beam of the flashlight into the dark space underneath. There, glittering in the light, was the fatty tumor, a great yellow mass of tiny globules that looked somewhat like a large bunch of very small grapes.

159

Two neighboring ladies had come in to help if needed. I gave one the retractor to hold, keeping the muscle drawn to one side. The other held the flashlight while I began to remove the tumor. There was a central stem to which the yellow globules were attached, and from which they parted company on the slightest provocation. Some would roll into obscure corners and had to be removed one at a time. Others were embedded in the muscle and had to be dug out.

It took four hours. By the time it was over I was not only exhausted but miserable. My throat hurt worse than ever and my bones ached.

I went into the next room, poured water into a basin, and had just begun to clean up when there was a pounding on the front door and a voice calling my name. I went out to find a small colored boy who had gone almost white with terror. "Come quick to de clinic, Doctuh! De locomotive run over de brakeman! He on de porch and his liver's in his hat!"

I went, with the blood of my recent labors still on my hands.

The locomotive was standing on the rails in front of the clinic. There was a crowd around it and a crowd on the clinic porch, all strangely quiet. They made way for me.

The man was obviously dead. He lay on his back, his torso completely crushed. On the floor beside him, upside down, was his hat; it was filled to the brim, not with his liver but with his lungs. Even so, what I remember most was the look on the man's bloodstained face: a twisted, ghastly, contorted expression of mingled agony and terror.

I had to take charge of an immediate, preliminary inquest. It had been the brakeman's custom, I was told, to ride on the step at the front of the engine. Apparently (no one had actually seen the accident) he had slipped and fallen directly between but not on the tracks. The locomotive was driven by a huge cogwheel underneath and very close to the ground. This passed over the brakeman's body from groin to head. It crushed his chest, forcing his lungs up out of his mouth and, incredibly, into his hat fallen on the ground beside him.

160

By the time the inquest was over it was 4 o'clock. I had not yet had any lunch. My throat was almost too sore to swallow and when I checked my temperature it was 101°. I made my weary way to the home of Mrs. Nellie Cash with the idea of getting something to eat, then returning to the *Green Cross* and going to bed.

Nellie Cash was a close friend of Viola's and had volunteered, when Viola and Gayle had to return to Marsh Harbour, to give me a hot lunch on the days I worked at the clinic. Now she took one look at me as I tottered into her house and said, "Evans, you ought to call a doctor."

"I will," I said. "Just as soon as I've had a bite to eat."

I don't remember what she gave me. Whatever it was, I'd got only a few mouthfuls down my aching throat when there was a knocking at the door. I heard Nellie arguing with someone, saying the doctor was sick, he could do no more work today. If the person would come back tomorrow . . .

There was a wail and a man's voice saying, "He got to come now! My wife in some kind of spell. She can't move or say nothing. Maybe she dead!"

So I went. It was a half-hour walk and I found the woman lying perfectly motionless, rigid, in the middle of the family bed. But she was not dead. In fact her breathing and heartbeat seemed completely normal. Once, as I turned to question the husband, I thought I caught the flicker of an eyelid.

I put a thumb on her eye and tried to open it to examine her pupillary reaction. For a moment it would not open. Then the lid relaxed and moved back under my thumb. But the eye, instead of rolling aimlessly in its socket, stared directly and malevolently at me. For perhaps five seconds that eye and I stared at one another. I let go the lid. And still the eye looked at me for another second or two before the lid slowly closed.

My medical bag was on the floor at my feet. I bent over, soaked some cotton with spirits of ammonia, and with no warning held it under the lady's nose.

She exploded into a sitting position. Sputtering like a wet

161

motor, she knocked the cotton out of my hand, glared at me with an expression of pure hatred for an instant—then fell back into her swoon.

But the lady's lids were not shut as tightly as they had been; there was still a tiny slit of eye showing. "Your wife has had these spells before?" I asked the husband.

"Yes, Doctuh."

"This time, had you two been quarreling?"

"Yes, suh. We was having a kind of a row."

"And the other spells, did they come on when you had been fighting?"

He reflected a moment. "Dot's right, Doctuh. Now I think about it, it seem like every time we been fussing."

I picked up the cotton. "Don't you see her game? She does this just to scare you and make you give in. She's no more in a spell than you are. Watch—"

I moved the cotton toward her nose. It never got there. The lady came out of the bed as if sprung from a trap, shouting and shaking both fists. For an instant I thought she was going to attack me, while the husband sat with his mouth wide open in amazement. Then he too was on his feet, he and the lady screaming in one another's face.

I tapped him on the shoulder. When he turned I said, "Next time call a preacher, not a doctor." Then I picked up my bag and departed. I hadn't been paid and I didn't want to be paid. My throat was raw and my head hurt and my bones hurt and I just wanted to get back to the *Green Cross* and go to bed.

It wasn't to be easy. By the time I reached the dock it was well after dark. There was no moon and I could barely see the outlines of my dinghy. I stepped down into it, and into water up to my knees. While I stood there, too surprised, sick, and angry to react, the dinghy sank slowly to the bottom, plunging me chest-deep in water.

It took most of my strength to climb back on the dock. What had happened was fairly obvious: the dinghy had drifted under the dock at low tide; as the tide rose the boat was trapped there and flooded to the gunwales.

162

There was a barge tied at the end of the dock. A couple of the crewmen helped me refloat my dinghy. Wearily I sculled out to the *Green Cross,* which was anchored about two hundred yards off the dock, and climbed aboard. Home sweet home, I thought, and wondered if I would have the strength to give myself any treatment before falling in bed. It seemed a monumental decision and my brain worked slowly at reaching it.

"Doctor!" a voice shouted from the dock. "Emergency, Doctor!"

Fortunately this one was brought to me, because I don't think I could have gone to him. It was a man with his arm slashed open from the wrist to the elbow. Oddly enough, it had happened while digging the grave for the brakeman.

The batteries on the *Green Cross* were down and I had almost no light. But there were four flashlights among the men who had brought the patient. It gave the scene a strange, theatrical effect. There was an artery severed and someone had applied a tourniquet. Blood leaped when it was released. I was lucky to catch the artery with my hemostatic forceps on the first try, then tie it off with catgut. The gash was deep, but clean. It took seventeen sutures to close.

When the men were ready to leave I asked them to wait just a moment. I had one more patient to treat by the light of their torches: I gave myself a shot of penicillin, and after that I honestly don't remember. But next morning when I awoke the sun was shining and my sore throat had vanished.

It was shortly after this that Dr. Ejnar Gottlieb arrived. He was a tall, well-built man in his early thirties, with a slow smile and a thick German accent. I showed him around the clinic that now was to be his.

He was an extremely competent, well-trained M.D., friendly, happy to be here, almost as delighted with the tropics as I had been on my first visit to Nassau. I wondered whether he knew as little of what he was getting into.

The date of Dr. Gottlieb's arrival had been known, so I had the *Green Cross* ready to sail. All that remained was to pay

163

Nellie Cash for the meals I had eaten at her home. Several times I had mentioned this, but she had always put off naming an amount. Now I went by her home, but she was out.

I took some money in a sealed envelope over to the store Gus Cash, her husband, managed, and asked him to give it to her. Then I went back to the *Green Cross*. There was a short wait to catch the tide. As I was about to weigh anchor Gus Cash arrived on the dock, calling me. I sculled in. "Nellie's fixed a box of sandwiches for your supper," he said.

That night when I opened the box I found sandwiches all right. Also the envelope of money.

When it comes to kindness, there are some people you can't catch up with, and just knowing them, having their respect, being friends with them, gives a man a good feeling. I sat in the stern of the *Green Cross* and thought about this, and ate the sandwiches, and watched the moon come up. It glowed very softly on the sail and on the lip of water that curled from the bow. I thought about getting home to Viola and Gayle and I thought of all the other strange ports we could reach in the *Green Cross*, under moonlit or sunlit skies, across blue or white water. And it occurred to me it was a cry-baby and cowardly thing to wail, as do so many of our frustrated city-dwellers, that life has no deep meaning or reasoned plan that the individual can fathom. For even if this be true, and no matter what life signifies, including nothing, it can still be a rather wonderful adventure, if you allow yourself to adventure in it.

20

The Deep Blue Ocean and
the Shallow Banks

I SOLD Gun Bluff.

Even now I cannot think about it without emotion, a sense of loss both wistful and deeply poignant. In one way at least, Gun Bluff had been my first true love and there could never be another. Even so, I realized that my life had become more or less settled around Marsh Harbour. I knew Viola could never be happy at Gun Bluff, isolated from her family and friends, and that was quite understandable. Also, no matter how I loved the place, I had to admit it was not the spot to raise Gayle. So when I got an offer from an American doctor, I took it.

Perhaps the sale left me more than normally restless, though as I have said, I was—am—usually willing to go dashing off to any island I have never seen before. Also, I was intensely excited about the *Green Cross*. It was not only the answer to an ancient dream of mine; it was the key to a thousand things I wanted to see and do. I had been living in the Bahamas now for ten years, but had seen only a fraction of them. I yearned to see them all.

Viola and I talked it over. But trying to explain the wanderlust to a person not affected by it is like trying to explain atomic fission to freshman students: they can accept the fact it exists because there is proof, but they don't understand it. Viola said that if I was anxious to go sailing on the *Green Cross*

165

there were a lot of places I could visit in half a day, a day at the most, and come home again. I said I had already been to those places, an argument which made no sense to Viola. She reminded me I had been interested in reviving her father's plantation. I pointed out that the plantation was in a part of Abaco so difficult to reach that transportation problems made it impossible to revive. For better or worse, I said, I was an out-island doctor, and there were a great many of the out-islands that seriously needed a doctor's help.

Eventually I carried the day. And on July 9, 1949, I set out alone on what was supposed to be a trip of "a few weeks." As I sailed out of the harbor I wrote in my diary: "Just how far, or just where I will go, will be determined by circumstances as I go along."

My first stops were the nearby cays I had visited before: Guana Cay, Green Turtle Cay, Coopers Town. I doctored a day or two in each, and moved on. This was a route I had covered before, on my trips back and forth to Grand Bahama.

Near the settlement of Crown Haven there is a spot where Little Abaco is only about fifty feet wide and through this the government has blasted a channel. I passed through and within a few minutes was on the south side of Abaco, in what to me were new waters. I turned south with the intention of visiting Mores Island.

Next day I wrote in my diary: "The wind was ahead yesterday and rather light, so I made extremely slow headway." It was a sentence that, with variations, I was going to repeat over and over because much of my course now would take me into the teeth of the prevailing summer winds. But if the prevailing wind was against me, the prevailing weather was delightful. Much of the time I let the *Green Cross* steer herself. I stretched comfortably on deck and read from the medical books I had brought.

And so I came into Mores Island and the settlement of Hard Bargain. I dropped anchor a hundred yards offshore and was still furling my sail when I heard someone shout, "Hey, you! Come in here!"

It was a large black woman. She stood on the beach with her fists on her hips, her head and shoulders back, a sort of Mussolini-like pose. "You!" she bellowed.

"What do you want?" I called.

"I want you should come here, now!"

I am an at least moderately mild man. I consider myself slow to anger. But nobody likes to be screamed at and ordered around by a total stranger. "I'll come when you learn manners," I snapped, and went below.

A few minutes later I heard a dinghy come alongside, then heard the woman sputtering and shouting even as she crawled over the rail, "You de Crown doctuh. You got to come when de people call you!"

Oh no! I thought. Not again. Yet I honestly think that for a moment I was sorrier for the unknown Crown doctuh who had to face this attitude most of the time in his work than for myself. (However, the Crown doctor had his own way of striking back, as I learned later: he sometimes refused to use his stethoscope. And how was a patient going to get any benefit out of a doctor who wouldn't take time to sound him and learn which way his blood ran?)

Now, uninvited, the dark lady crowded her way into my cabin. "I goin' to report you to de commissioner," she declared.

"All right," I said. "But let's get one thing straight first. I am not the Crown doctor. I don't give away medicine or shillings. Now what, if anything, do you want?"

"I want a t'rupence of salts."

I got my box of Epsom salts and ladled threepence worth into a bag. Holding it I asked, "Have you brought any money?"

"No, I ain' bring no money. You supposed to give me dis free."

I wasn't going to argue with her. I just poured the salts back in the box.

For a moment she looked almost apoplectic. Then from a pocket in her dirty dress she took out a still dirtier handkerchief, untied a knot in one corner, took out a threepence piece, and slammed it on my table. I put the coin in my pocket and once more ladled out the Epsom salts.

When my first patient had departed I went ashore in my dinghy to pass the word that "a doctuh done reach," even though most of the people, by that mysterious grapevine that operates in the Bahamas, already knew that the boat with the green cross on it housed a doctor.

If there was ever a properly named place, Hard Bargain was it. I had never seen any other spot in the Bahamas quite like it, and praise God for that. The dirt street was littered with rubbish. Many houses were tumble-down shacks, their yards even more filthy than the street. Any tree or flower or shrub or blade of grass that grew apparently did it against the wishes of the people. The whole place had a look of incredible poverty. Yet I knew from what I had heard that during the crawfish season, which was from December through mid-March, the men of Mores Island made good money. Very good money indeed, sometimes as much as fifteen to twenty pounds a day—more money in a day possibly than some of the men on Crooked Island might see in a year. But it must have all been spent on rum. It seemed to me that fifty percent of the population, men and women alike, were drunk. Certainly the sounds of brawling blew as steadily through the town as did the trade winds. I did not dare leave the *Green Cross* for long lest the whole boat be stolen.

And the people, it quickly turned out, were as bad off physically as they looked. Venereal diseases and tuberculosis were particularly rampant. And despite the fact that rum flowed freely, malnutrition was widespread. Once I threw a piece of moldy bread overboard and was startled to see a man dive after it. Neither the mold nor salt water was enough to overcome his hunger.

This abject poverty presented me with a very serious problem. It does not seem to me unreasonable to feel that any man or woman who can manage to stay drunk a good part of the time should also manage to pay a small doctor bill. Yet the literal truth is that many of the persons who came to me in

168

serious need of medical attention, some of whom had been drinking and some of whom hadn't, actually had no money. None at all. Some would have two, three, or four shillings— and need at least ten to twelve shillings' worth of medicine. I tried to be as diplomatic as possible, to judge, as well as I was capable of judging, each individual case. It is not an easy or pleasant thing to find oneself forced into this sort of God-like position. I was too aware of my own shortcomings, of the hundred and one things about each individual I did not and could not know. I was gnawed at by fear that I gave to the wrong persons and denied the right ones. Yet all I could do was my best.

My third day at Mores Island I moved to the neighboring settlement, The Bight, a spot every bit as desolate as Hard Bargain. Even as I anchored a man sculled out and asked me to visit his brother who was seriously ill. I went with him to a shack on the edge of town. My first awareness, going through the door, was of an almost unbearable stench. It hit me, stopped me as if I had run against a wall. Then the door closed; the room was darkened and, coming out of the brilliant sunshine, I was momentarily blinded. Now with the stench I was aware of heat, a dead, stifling, breathless heat, and also of a dull drone that was like the roar of a distant sea until I recognized it as the drone of a multitude of flies and felt them brushing against my face and hands.

As my eyes adjusted to the darkness the details of the room came clear. On one side was a bed: a rumpled pile of straw and filthy quilts. In the middle of this lay a gaunt, emaciated man, coughing constantly. I did not even need to go near him to know he was dying of pulmonary tuberculosis. He lay on his back, his head turned to one side. As he coughed, he made feeble efforts to spit. The phlegm had spread over his face and throat; it had clotted along the edge of the bed and lay in a pool on the floor. On this, around it, and in a dim droning mass around the room went the flies. On a box beside the bed sat the man's wife, nursing a baby. Three children, ranging in age from one to three, played on the floor, crawling back and forth through the pool of tuberculous phlegm. There was a table with dirty dishes and partially eaten food, almost hidden by the flies. And on another box, against the far wall, sat an old woman. She made no sound but rocked gently back and forth. Her face had a placid, almost happy look; her eyes gazed far into space. On the floor beside her was a bottle of rum. Now and then, without ceasing her gentle rocking, without looking, she reached down and found the bottle and took a small swallow.

There was little I could do for the man. But I called the wife outside and tried to explain to her the difference between the air blowing off the water and the air inside her closed house. I tried to explain germs and how flies could spread them and the danger to her children. She listened. "Yessuh," she said whenever I paused and waited for an answer.

"You will let some air in the house?"

"Yessuh."

"You will get your husband a pot or pan of some kind to spit into? And then keep it covered so the flies can't get at it."

"Yessuh."

"And you will clean him? Clean the bed, clean the floor, scrub it, and keep it clean?"

"Yessuh."

"Do you know what *clean* is? Do you know what I mean?"

"Oh yessuh."

She looked straight at me. She seemed intelligent. She seemed to understand. And yet I knew with a terrible and futile certainty that all I said went in one ear and out the other.

I walked back toward the *Green Cross*. On the way I passed the public well and paused to look into it, wondering about the settlement's water supply. There were rocks jutting out from the side of the well. The water in the bottom was only a few inches deep. In this stood an old woman, her dress done up around her waist. Her legs and feet were covered with open sores. In one hand she had a slop pail and in the other a dirty rag. The water in the well was not deep enough to dip the pail into; instead she dipped the rag into it, then squeezed the rag over the pail. I asked what she was going to do with the water.

"Oh dis good drinking water," she said, and generously held the pail up toward me. "You does want a drink?"

"No, thank you. I—"

But what was there to say? I went on, down the dirty street, past the dirty tumble-down shacks with the naked and dirty children playing in the yards under a blue and white sky in sight of turquoise and silver water. What was the difference between Mores Island and Crooked Island or Long Cay? Climatically, physically, they were very much the same. Their people were of the same origin.

I didn't know the answer.

When the stream of patients at Mores Island slackened, I weighed anchor and went south. A short morning's sail and the palm-fringed outline of Gorda Cay was visible. About a mile offshore I was hailed by a fisherman in a dinghy who came alongside. "You is the doctuh?"

"Yes."

"You is goin' to Gorda Cay?"

"That's where I'm headed."

"Well praise de Lord! Plenty peoples want to see you." He tied his dinghy to mine and climbed aboard the *Green Cross*. "I'm goin' to pilot you in."

His name was Felix Sands and I was very glad to have him aboard, especially so as we began to work our way through a channel so narrow it would have been frightening without a pilot. Ashore I could see a scattering of tiny thatched huts but no real houses, and I asked my guide about the people.

"Oh," he said, "these peoples all from Sandy Point on Abaco. Nobody live year-round on Gorda; they only come here to farm."

"They don't come from Mores Island?"

He gave me a quick look as if uncertain whether I was joking or being insulting. "Doctuh," he said, "you see that deep blue ocean?" He pointed. "And you see these yellow shallow banks yonder? Doctuh, the peoples to Sandy Point ain' no more like the peoples to Mores Island than that deep blue ocean like those yellow mud banks."

"But why?"

"I don't know why. They just different."

It was not an explanation, but it proved to be the truth. The thatched huts in which the people lived were little more than shelters, but they were intended only for temporary use during the farming season. They were scrupulously clean. There were flowers and fruit trees. There was a distinct air of industry, and despite Felix Sands' welcome, only a moderate amount of illness. In two days I had sounded everybody who came to be sounded, and so sailed on to Sandy Point.

Sandy Point is near the southwest tip of Great Abaco. Now there is a Nassau-owned fishing lodge there that attracts visitors from the States as well as the Bahamas; but at this time of my first visit it was an all colored settlement. It was also one of the most picturesque spots in all the Bahamas and possibly in all the world. Certainly it looked like some movie's idealized version of a South Sea island village. There was the beautiful beach, the coconut palms rustling gently in the trade wind, the small, neatly painted houses surrounded by clean and flower-filled yards. And Felix Sands' statement about the people of Sandy Point and those of Mores Island can be illustrated by a single incident.

I reached Sandy Point in late July and was kept busy for several days with the usual stream of patients. I did not, however, expect any patients on August 1. August 1 commemorates the emancipation of British slaves in 1838. Among the colored folk in the Bahamas it is a great national, racial holiday and in most places is turned into a drunken orgy. But August 1 at Sandy Point I was awakened, as usual, by the sound of hammers. There was some construction going on near the dock and I looked out to see the carpenters working industriously away. I also found patients waiting to put me to work and I asked one of them if Sandy Point people did not celebrate the holiday.

172

"Oh," she said scornfully. "We don't have time for that foolishness. Peoples here have work to do."

It made me ponder. As I have said, Sandy Point looked like a dream of a South Seas paradise where nobody ever worked or even thought of working. Yet here the people were working, and I knew that at Hard Bargain, which looked as if it had been cursed by both man and God, the people weren't working. There seemed to be, as Percy Cavill once said, a moral here, and, as best I could figure, it went like this: even in a tropical paradise there is a certain amount of work that has to be done, because without work even paradise can degenerate into the cesspools of Hard Bargain.

But there were also problems at Sandy Point. One of my patients was a young mother with her baby in her arms.

"You does have paregoric?" she said.

I did, but before selling it inquired what she wanted it for.

"Oh, Doctuh," she said, "dot de best baby medicine I ever see. Last time my baby get a crying spell I just give him paregoric. And he went right off to sleep. He slept all night and all de next day and next night. Doctuh, paregoric one wonderful medicine for a baby!"

"How much did you give the baby?"

"A tablespoonful. Dot was all."

That was all—about four times the average adult dose! Carefully I explained to her that it was a wonder her baby had not slept forever. She listened, her eyes getting larger in her face and holding her baby tighter as I talked. And in the end I sold her a bottle of Castoria instead of paregoric.

2 1

From Sandy Point to Nassau

From Sandy Point I sailed southwest with no problems except headwinds, or no winds at all, to Lignum Vitae Cay in the Berry Islands. This was a tiny settlement and it did not take long to "sound the peoples," then move on to Bullocks Harbour and more work.

Here I was told that going south it would be necessary to sail outside, in the open ocean, because the inside channel was both tricky and shallow. In fact, off Ambergris Cay it was only about four feet deep. The *Green Cross* drew three feet nine inches. Yet I didn't like the idea of sailing in the open ocean along a dangerous lee shore.

Caught between an inside devil and the outside deep blue sea I chose the devil. In my diary for August 14, 1949 I wrote:

11:00 A.M.   I am now on my way through the rather intricate inside channel of the Berry Islands. Some of the folks at Bullocks Harbour think I won't make it. Maybe they are right. Tide will be high at noon, and I left Bullocks Harbour at 8 A.M. So a good part of my way will be a high tide. If I stick somewhere this afternoon when the tide ebbs, I'll just drop anchor and wait until tomorrow's flood tide. (As Percy Cavill said, time in the out-islands doesn't matter.) The wind is partly ahead so I am managing with long and short tacks. I spend most of my time standing up bow watching for banks and blue channels.

Same evening.   Well, I didn't get stuck. Ambergris Cay

approached, passed, receded, and nothing happened. I came into Little Harbour Cay just at sunset.

Now the worst of the Berry Island passage lay behind me. My next stop was at Little Whale Cay, certainly one of the most beautiful of all the Bahama Islands.

Little Whale was, and I believe still is, owned by a Mr. Wallace Groves, an American financier who also owned Pine Ridge. The whole cay had been converted into a kind of tropical fairyland. About the estate itself there were great masses of flowers and groves of trees and long sweeps of grassy lawn. And practically the whole thing, the whole island in fact, was an elaborate aviary. Peacocks and flamingos strutted on the lawns along with golden pheasants. Ducks and geese circled overhead and in the trees beautiful, multicolored birds I could not name made loud noises. There was also a tiny native settlement that looked like something Disney might have thought up. On the other hand, there was no doctor; I put in several busy days.

I had written Mr. Groves about a month earlier, telling him of my proposed visit. He was not there, but his manager, a Frenchman named Leschevin, made me welcome and installed me in a luxurious guest house. I not only had electric lights and hot water, but fresh milk from the island's own cow.

Late one afternoon while I was there a Miami yacht tied up at the dock. Aboard were three marine scientists making a survey of game fish in the area. That night the Leschevins had us all for dinner. It was beautifully served. Both Mr. and Mrs. Leschevin spoke English with a noticeable French accent and they were as gracious and charming as any legend of French hospitality. The marine scientists, intense, sunburned men, talked about their work, tracing the migratory habits of various bill fish. I sat there listening, and eating Mrs. Leschevin's French cooking, and then I told them something about my work: the moldy bread I had gnawed on a few days before at Hard Bargain and thrown overboard, the well at The Bight —touching on it lightly, for this seemed hardly the time to go

175

into details. It was all a very pleasant evening and it reminded me, at least from the point of view of being an oddly assorted company gathered by chance in a remote place, of the dinner Percy Cavill and I had eaten with Captain Rees.

From Little Whale Cay I moved on to Bird Cay where, to my surprise and delight, I discovered Mr. Forsyth. He had come here, he told me, to recover from a recent illness; but it seemed impossible to think of him as having ever been sick. In his seventies, he was as lean, brisk, and energetic as ever. And just as full of information. I mentioned that sand flies sometimes gave me a hard time on my boat; I had screens that kept out the mosquitoes, but the tiny sand flies came right through them. "They should be no problem," Mr. Forsyth said. "Mix a bit of your motor oil with an equal amount of kerosene and sponge it on your screens with a bit of cotton. That stops them."

And it did! Ten years I had been in the Bahamas, eaten alive now and then, without acquiring this simple bit of information.

From Bird Cay I sailed directly to Nassau, where I tied up at the dock of Mr. Charles Turtle. I sent Viola a telegram saying I was safe so far, bought her a vase of a kind I knew she wanted for her flowers, visited a dentist to have my teeth checked over, then went shopping for general supplies: mast grease, rope, a machete, a new clock, drugs, and groceries. From the post office I got an accumulation of mail and went back to the *Green Cross* to read it.

Tripsie, Viola wrote, had another litter of puppies. Mother Sawyer was as well as could be expected. Gayle was beginning to take a few steps; she could point to my picture and say "Daddy." Viola herself was well and busy but missed me and when was I coming home?

I sat there with the letters in my hands and realized I still had no master plan. I had been gone almost six weeks. I had covered a number of the islands I had never seen before. I was having a wonderful time. But I missed Viola. I missed her

176

very much. I missed being with Gayle as she learned to walk and talk. I—

Someone called my name and there were footsteps on deck. It was Mr. Turtle.

Charles Turtle was a short, suntanned, gray-haired man of about sixty. I had met him while the *Green Cross* was being built and he had given me a set of charts of his own making, the very best charts ever made of the Bahamian waters, so far as I know. He had sailed these waters all his life and there was nobody who knew them better. Now he began to tell me about the cays to the south and his experiences among them. We broke out the charts and he went over them: here there had been a well dug since the charts were made; there the channel had shifted a bit to the west.

He stayed for two hours. When he had gone ashore I sat in my cabin with the charts on the table, and with Viola's letters on the bunk. First I would look at one, then I would look at the other. There were a lot of islands I wanted to see. And at the same time I wanted to go home. There were islands where the Crown doctor rarely went and where my services would be badly needed. And there were Gayle and Viola. I looked at the chart, at all the cays that stretched from Nassau to Crooked Island. I'll go as far as Great Exuma, I thought. I'll work hard all the way. And then home.

With a decision made, I turned on the radio for the weather report: the first hurricane of the season was brewing somewhere around Puerto Rico, its course and intensity as yet uncertain.

Next day I moved the *Green Cross* up to the Yacht Haven dock in order to get gas and water. The dock, as I approached, was completely deserted and blowing my horn did no good. Across the end of the dock a swank, millionaire-class yacht was tied, her stern projecting out beyond the side where I wanted to secure the *Green Cross*. Sitting in a deck chair was a bulbous-bellied, thick-lipped man wearing a white suit and dark glasses. As I blew my horn his face turned slowly toward

177

the *Green Cross*. I couldn't see his eyes because of the dark glasses, but his lips curled in something very close to a sneer.

"Can you take my line?" I called.

He leaned forward, his fat hands folded on his belly, and spat over the rail.

I decided he looked like a gangster, or something found under a rock. However, I had no time to ponder on which. About forty feet away was another yacht, this one with a great expanse of glass windows and nobody aboard. My plan was to dock the *Green Cross* between these two, and after what I considered some pretty good maneuvering she was almost in her space—when the motor cut off. The *Green Cross* was drifting, slowly but implacably forward, her bowsprit not more than two feet from the big glass windows of the deserted yacht.

There was no time to race forward and try to hold the boat off physically. Frantically I pushed the starter button. To my mingled relief and amazement, for once the motor caught with a roar. I threw the clutch in reverse, and saw the bowsprit touch gently as a feather against the glass and move back from it.

Now four men were running out on the dock, shouting. But by the time they arrived I was secure. One of the men began to apologize for not having seen me come in. "My motor cut off on me," I said. I looked over to the other yacht where the fat slug of a man still sat with his hands folded on his belly. "I'd asked that—gentleman," I said, making sure I spoke loudly enough to be heard, "to take my line. But I suppose he is too fat to get out of his chair." Then I spat.

The fat man did not move. He sat there, his face showing no more expression than the dark glasses.

By the time I had taken on my supplies and dropped back down the channel to Mr. Turtle's dock there had been a number of new hurricane reports, but just how close to Nassau the storm would come was still uncertain. I talked the matter over with Mr. Turtle. Nassau is a poor spot for boats in a hurricane. On the other hand, there were, Mr. Turtle said, a number of excellent anchorages in the Exuma Cays. He marked several of them on the chart for me. The problem was: would I have time to reach the cays?

A new report said the storm, if it continued on its present course, would pass north of Abaco and that Nassau and waters to the south would not be affected. But I wanted to be certain. For five more hours I watched the barometer and listened to reports.

By 10 o'clock I was sure the hurricane would pass well to the north. At 2:30 A.M. I weighed anchor under a clear sky with only a light wind blowing and headed for the Exuma Cays, hoping to make Allen's Cay for my first night's anchorage.

22

Hurricane at Shroud Cay

ALL morning my barometer showed no drop. The hurricane advisory reports continued to track the storm well to the north and by noon I was certain it no longer presented any threat to my course. But the wind was ahead and light, and my progress was slow.

About 1 P.M. the wind began to pick up. Within a few minutes it was blowing hard, and by 1:15 it was raining. The weather reports still tracked the hurricane away from the Bahamas, so I was sure this was no more than a local squall. But it was quite a squall. I lowered my mainsail, then went ahead through wind and rain with my two small sails and the engine. The waves built quickly, high and choppy. I thought of the old *Cheerful* and of the days when five minutes of seas like this and I would have been hanging helplessly over the rail. Now I found it stimulating and began to sing.

Singing has never been my forte. In range of human ears I am inclined to refrain. But on the *Green Cross*, with no one to hear me, I often let go, usually with songs of my own composing. These were frequently aimed at satirizing certain beliefs, religious notions, and customs which some of my Marsh Harbour friends took far more seriously than I did—and probably it is just as well that I only sang them while alone. Singing, I went on through the squall and into lovely weather beyond it. Shortly after 3 P.M. I sighted land (Ship Channel Cay) and a few hours later, under a thunderous, sky-filling sunset, I anchored at Allen's Cay. Radio reports said the hurricane had continued north and was well out of the Bahama area.

Next morning there was news of another color. A second hurricane had been born, full grown, between two hundred and three hundred miles to the southeast and was heading straight for me. Gale-force winds ranged far ahead of the storm's eye. As well as I could figure from the report, I had about twenty-four to thirty hours in which to find a safe anchorage.

Hastily I consulted the charts on which Mr. Turtle had marked all the hurricane harbors, with explanatory notes written beside them. The nearest was at Norman's Cay, but the entrance was intricate. I would have to manage it alone, and I was afraid of catching ashore in some exposed place with no chance to get off before the storm struck.

The next anchorage was at Shroud Cay, about fifteen miles from where I was. I didn't care for the name of the place—it just didn't sound like a hurricane haven—but I had no other choice. The wind was fair and I ran the distance in a little over three hours.

"Shroud Cay," says the *Yachtsman's Guide to the Bahamas*, "is, in reality, an archipelago of small cays divided by swamps and creeks." To me, skirting slowly along the shore, it seemed nothing but mangrove swamp and no place I could really care for at any time. But finally I found the creek Mr. Turtle had

180

marked, entered, and dropped anchor just inside the mouth. Quickly, I jumped in my dinghy and went exploring.

The tide was low and still ebbing, so the creek, except for the mouth, was very shallow. But well inland I found a deep hole protected by high land. This was the anchorage Mr. Turtle had recommended and it was an excellent one. I went back to the *Green Cross,* planning to bring it up the creek with the high tide first thing next morning.

Now I do not want to pick any quarrel with the hurricane-warning service. It does the best job it humanly can. But predicting the future of a hurricane is not a job for human beings. A hurricane's course is as erratic and unpredictable as that of a baby just learning to walk: a gigantic, monstrous infant that toddles a few steps in one direction, tearing up trees and knocking over houses instead of breaking bric-a-brac, then pausing, rocking back and forth in the same spot, staggering to one side to casually destroy a town, before plunging forward in a wild, falling gallop.

Just before dark my radio announced that the storm had begun one of its forward gallops. Gale-force winds were predicted for my area long before morning.

There was still some daylight; the tide had turned and was coming in and I determined to go with it. I got up the anchor, throttled the engine down slow, moving chiefly with the tide itself. Several times I touched bottom, but the tide was rising rapidly and I was never caught for more than a moment. With the last bit of daylight I reached the big hole I had selected for my anchorage. By the time everything was secure it was pitch dark.

I went below and had supper. I watched the barometer, which stayed placidly steady. Outside only a light breeze blew and the sky was clear. I noted the conditions in my diary, added, "I feel safe for the night at any rate," and went to sleep.

The next entry in my diary was:

August 25. At 11 A.M. this morning the United States Weather Bureau issued the reassuring report that the storm has shifted to the northwest and the Bahamas are thought to be out of danger. The tide was still high, so with a sigh of relief I took up my anchors and came back to the mouth of the creek.

My plan at this point was to continue south, now that the hurricane was gone. But there was still a hard wind blowing, harder in fact than at any time during the night. Outside the creek mouth the sea was a white rage. So I decided to stay where I was until things calmed down a bit.

I stayed there all afternoon, but instead of calming the wind grew stronger. And at 5 P.M. came the next hurricane advisory. That monstrous infant had once more toddled off in a new direction. Now the center of the storm was due to strike the Exuma Cays sometime that same night. Indeed, what I was already getting was the forward fringe of it. Within a few hours, the prediction said, the winds should reach one hundred miles an hour, or more.

It was out of the question to remain where I was, and equally out of the question to get back to the anchorage I had so prematurely left. True, I had made it in yesterday just before dark; but today the tide was forty-five minutes later. That would make it pitch dark before the water was deep enough to get through. And there was no way of knowing how hard the storm would be blowing at that time. Already my spars were shaking before forty-knot gusts.

Just inland from the creek's mouth there was a narrow place where mangroves grew close to both sides. A sandbar crossed the creek here. The water over it was too shallow to let me pass and would be for some time. But in the other direction, beyond the creek's mouth, was the open sea. And I didn't have the faintest intention of going in that direction.

I tied the middle of both my hawsers around the Samson post. This left half of each hawser running to an anchor; the other half would be free to tie into the mangroves. I dropped the jib boom and tied it to the Samson post, furled and tied all sails, including the dinghy sail. I took the oar out of the

182

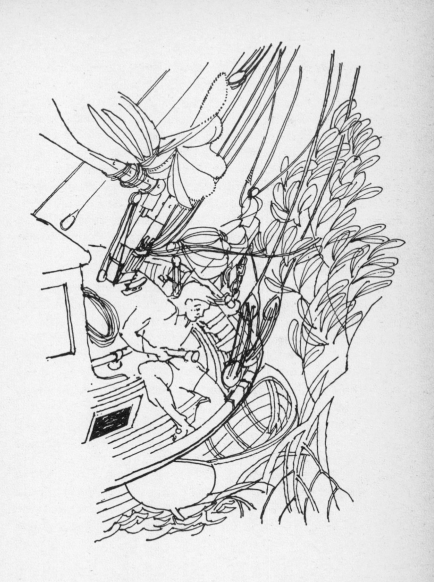

dinghy and put it in the *Green Cross*, thinking it would be safer there. Then I started the motor and headed up the creek.

Already it was getting dark. There was no rain as yet but the wind had begun to howl in the mangroves and hiss at my mast. The tide was running in, fast, carrying the *Green Cross* with it. Ahead of me in the thickening gloom I could barely see where the water rippled over the sandbar.

I pulled my throttle wide open and headed for the ripples. The inrushing tide added speed. The *Green Cross* struck the sandbar close to the right bank of the creek, slid well up on it, and stuck firmly. I threw my forty-pound grapnel into the mangroves on the starboard side, then took the loose end of that hawser, waded into the mangroves, and tied it fast. Back on the *Green Cross*, I dropped my big anchor and the loose end of that hawser into the water on my port bow and followed them over the side.

By now the water in the deepest part of the creek was up to my chest and running so swiftly it almost swept me off my feet. But I struggled across to the bank on the port side, dropped the anchor among the mangroves, and made the loose end of the hawser secure to some roots.

The darkness was complete now. It was a thick, solid darkness in which, literally, I could not see my hand before my face. I had to follow the anchor line back to the *Green Cross*, pulling myself hand over hand. I climbed aboard and, moving like a blind man, found my flashlight.

The first thing the beam showed me was that my two lines to starboard had gone slack. The ones to port, over which I had just climbed, were taut. But the rising tide and a shift in the wind had swung the *Green Cross* about until the starboard moorings hung useless. With a still farther shift in wind and tide they would become far worse than useless; they might well pull the house off the boat. I was going to have to put all four moorings on the port side.

Once more I went over the rail. Now the water was up to my chin but I got ashore, took up both lines, and brought them back aboard.

Since the *Green Cross* drew only three feet nine inches I figured she must be afloat and I started the engine, intending to move her to the other side of the creek before putting the grapnel over again. But when I threw in the clutch she did not budge. Her stern was to the incoming tide; she should have been surging forward with the tide. But she was steady as Gibraltar. I raced the motor. There was the vibration from the engine, and nothing else. Was my clutch working? Was my propeller turning? I checked. Nothing wrong here.

Once more I went overboard, and into water over my head. There must be a log or some other obstruction lodged under her, I thought. And there was only one way to find out.

I am not a good diver. I have a tendency to bob too quickly to the surface. But I took a long breath and dived, feeling my way under the stern, grabbing the bottom of the keel, and hauling myself forward. The tide pushed me and I moved fast, almost too fast, so that I was barely able to cling to the bow when I reached it. But from stern to stem the *Green Cross* had at least two feet of water between her keel and any obstruction. She was floating, and yet she would not move.

I pulled myself aboard and found the flashlight. There was still no rain; the beam of light hollowed the darkness like a tunnel drilled through black rock. In it I found my trouble. The painter to my dinghy had become tangled in a cluster of mangroves and it was this that held the *Green Cross*. I climbed over the side, swung along the painter to the dinghy, and tried to free it. The line was too taut and I realized it would have to be untied from the *Green Cross*.

Up to this point, I am fairly sure, I had been acting rationally and logically. From this point on is another matter. Perhaps it was the increasing violence of the wind and my own increasing excitement. Perhaps it was fatigue dulling my wits, although at the moment I was not aware of exhaustion. At any rate, hand over hand through the solid darkness I pulled myself back along the painter to the *Green Cross*. Hanging there on the port side near the stern, my feet in the water, arms and elbows on the deck, I set to work to untie the dinghy's painter

185

from the ringbolt. It was a slow job, and to save the batteries in the flashlight I turned it off and put it on the deck close in front of my chest. Finally I felt the knot loosen, and heaved a sigh of relief. It was my last one for some time.

Freed of the bond that had held her to the dinghy and the mangroves, the *Green Cross* leaped forward with the inrushing tide. For a split second I was conscious of grasping at the runaway boat with my left hand while clinging to the painter with my right. Then I plunged into the creek.

When I came up the *Green Cross* was gone. I was still holding to the painter with the tide beating at me as though to rip me away from it. Desperately, under water as much as I was above, I pulled myself back to the dinghy. Then, feeling my way, following the painter, I skirted back and forth through the mangroves until it was free.

And now what?

It was at this moment, faced with a major decision, that I first clearly realized how serious my position was. I was on an isolated cay, thirty miles from the nearest human being. Nobody in the world had the least idea of my whereabouts. I was separated from the *Green Cross* by the rushing black waters of the creek. At least I hoped she was somewhere on the opposite side, since my moorings on that side should have held her. But she was out of sight. In that darkness everything was out of sight. Also, the hurricane was now beginning to show her real teeth; the sound of it, a vast dull howling, filled the universe.

I couldn't stay here. One way or another, I had to try to reach the *Green Cross*. The only chance, I decided, was to take the dinghy and try to scull directly across the creek. That way the inward rush of the tide might sweep me alongside the larger boat.

At that moment, as if to punctuate my decision, the sky let loose a deluge of hurricane-driven rain. It lashed into me. It stung like fine shot. It would have blinded me if the darkness had not already done so.

I turned my back to it and reached into the dinghy for the
186

oar. I couldn't find it. Frantically my hand groped across the decking from one side to the other, back and forth. It wasn't there. And all at once I remembered I had put it on the *Green Cross*. For safety!

So there was swimming. I put the painter in my teeth, groped for the mangroves with one hand to make sure of direction, then struck out straight across the creek, using the Australian crawl. If only Percy Cavill could see me now, I thought. And thought: If only I could swim the way he did. God knows I was trying. I could feel the tide rushing around me, sweeping me up the creek. And yet, strange as it may be, I was not actually afraid. Instead I felt a kind of intoxicated excitement that was by no means unpleasant. I was conscious of battling against the storm and, even at that moment, sure I was going to win.

I could see nothing. My hand touched something solid. It was the *Green Cross*. Blindly I had come as straight to her as if I had been drawn by a magnet. My feet touched bottom and I stood there and tied the dinghy's painter to the ringbolt even before I climbed aboard.

There was still work to do. Finding the flashlight, I dropped the grapnel and the loose end of the hawser overboard and followed them. Here the water was neck deep even along the fringe of mangroves. I looped the hawser about a big cluster of roots and made it fast, then tried to secure the grapnel. The mangroves were too thick to let it through. I climbed into them, bracing as much against the tear of the wind and rain as against the slippery limbs. Holding the flashlight aloft with my left hand and the grapnel in my right, I executed a kind of squatting, feet-first dive, spreading the mangroves apart with my feet until I could work the grapnel through. And now for the first time I was afraid, not of the storm and water but of moray eels that often lurk in the mangroves and can rip a man's hand to ribbons in seconds. Every twisted root that glowed in the beam of the flashlight seemed to slash teeth at me.

But if there were eels in the mangroves that night they had

187

problems of their own. None of them bothered me. With the grapnel secure I climbed back aboard the *Green Cross* and lay down to rest.

And all at once I thought of something I had told myself back in Marsh Harbour while my boat was being built and the local chorus of Job's Comforters was declaring I would never learn to rule it: I should have sense enough to keep out of storms, I had thought. There is no need ever to be caught alone in a storm.

Somehow it didn't seem funny at the moment.

In dry clothes at last, I lay on my bunk in the cabin of the *Green Cross*, but I didn't sleep, exhausted as I was. Driven by the hurricane, a considerable amount of water found its way into the cabin with me. It dripped on my bunk in half a dozen places. About midnight I told myself, if I can't sleep I might as well get up and put all this down in my diary while it's fresh in my mind.

(As if I were ever going to forget it!)

Anyway, I wrote it down. The final paragraph read:

One A.M. The storm is still raging outside. The wind comes in terrifying gusts. Each time a gust strikes my spars, the boat quivers all over. I wonder whether Shroud Cay will be my shroud. The tide is now ebbing and the *Green Cross* is ashore and listing to starboard. She might blow away, but at least for the present she can't float away. I am keeping the radio tuned in for hurricane reports. I believe the peak of the storm should pass here about 4 A.M. I am going to try the starboard bunk this time. It should be a little drier. I want to get a wink of sleep. God knows I need it.

I didn't get much sleep. Just over the starboard bunk was the shelf for my medical books. With the boat leaning heavily on that side I was rolled down against this shelf and no matter how I tried to curl around it, the thing kept stabbing me in the ribs. Then about 2 o'clock an exceptionally fierce gust of wind hammered the boat. When it passed I took the flashlight and went outside. And there under my starboard bilge was the

188

dinghy. Some current had swung her alongside the *Green Cross* and now she was wedged between the mangroves and the slowly descending bilge of the big boat. As the tide ebbed and the boat leaned more and more, the dinghy would be crushed to splinters.

In my time I have been personally acquainted with a great many dinghies, and I have never known one that could not continually get itself and its owner into a mass of trouble. Indeed, I have long suspected that all dinghies are inhabited by demons, each one a sort of combination poltergeist, gremlin, and fury, and that these take a personal delight in thinking up new and fiendish situations. The current example was a good one; I couldn't let the dinghy be crushed because the *Green Cross* might be left too firmly aground for me to get her off. In that case the dinghy—demon-inhabited though she was— would be my only hope of escape.

So over the side I went and tried to pull her free. But it was no use. Between the mangroves and the boat she was held as firmly as in a vise. I began frantically to try to rip up the mangroves, then realized that if I could tear them up, the storm would have done it a long time ago.

So now what?

Among the supplies I had bought in Nassau there was a brand new machete, purchased from John S. George & Company. Hurriedly I climbed aboard, found it, and hurled myself once more at the mangroves, slashing at them with all my strength. And nothing happened. I didn't even seem to dent them. By the light of the flash I examined the blade. It had never been sharpened. The backside was almost as sharp as the edge.

Now I am not normally an excitable man. Until that moment I had held to the theory that to lose one's temper completely is not only uncivilized but unnecessary as well. At this point I abandoned the theory. I referred to John S. George & Company, owners and employees, past, present, and future, their ancestors and descendants even to the third and fourth generations, by a highly individual and choice assortment of

189

terms. Yet even as I exploded I also worked, harder than ever, slashing and hacking. Finally I cleared enough space to drag the dinghy out of danger.

Once more I climbed aboard and dried myself as well as possible. The storm was at its peak now. It shrieked, wailed, and screamed. It battered the *Green Cross* with flying debris. At times the whole boat shook like a wet dog drying itself beside a creek. I lay in my bunk, rolled close against the bookshelf, water dripping on me. So tired I could scarcely breathe, I was still unable to sleep.

About 7 A.M. I got up and went on deck. The wind still blew a gale, but far less than it had during the night. Most of the rain had stopped. The tide had turned once more and was flowing in and the *Green Cross* was almost upright.

The trouble was, she was lying parallel to the creek and very firmly ashore alongside the mangroves. Somehow I had to get her back into deep water, and I had to do it alone, since certainly there was nobody to help me. Here was one facet of seamanship Uncle Willie Roberts had not told me about.

But something had to be done, and quick.

23

Message to Viola

Obviously the first thing was to learn if the engine worked. It did. So I threw in the clutch and gave it full power. The *Green Cross* did not budge.

For the unknownth time I went over the side to examine the situation. There were no obstructions holding the boat, except the bottom. That was muddy and gave me some hope. Also, the tide was still coming in. I waited another fifteen minutes, started the engine, and tried again. This time she drove forward a few inches, and stopped. I reversed her, and she came astern about half a foot. Full speed ahead, full speed astern, back and forth I went. Gradually the *Green Cross* plowed a groove for herself almost ten feet long. In this she could move back and forth, but there was no way to make her jump out of the groove. I tried standing on the bow and pushing with a long pole. The pole merely sank in the mud.

Back home if something of the sort had happened to my automobile, I would have walked or caught a ride to the nearest phone and called the garage. On Shroud Cay there was no phone, no garage, nobody to catch a ride with; there wasn't even any place to walk. So I sat down and tried to think, and eventually I was hit with an idea.

I took up my moorings, sculled out to midstream in a direct line with my stern, and dropped my big anchor. Back on the *Green Cross* I drew the anchor line taut and threw a bight around my mizzenmast. Now when I started my motor and drove the boat forward in its groove the line exerted a tremendous sideways pull against the mizzenmast—so powerful that my stern was dragged to port, widening the groove by a foot or more. I came astern, shortened the bight around the mast, and went ahead again. Repeating this over and over, I inched closer and closer to freedom. Finally, with one last surge, the stern dragged clear and I was floating again. At almost that exact moment the tide began to ebb. With it I went to the creek's mouth, and anchored.

The wind still blew in gusts but the sun was out. I brought my soaked clothes and bedding and books on deck and secured them against the wind. I went below to clean and dry things there as best I could. I was exhilarated, still too excited to be exhausted, and as I looked back on the night just passed it seemed only a wonderfully exciting and satisfying adventure, a kind of gigantic lark. Now that the danger was over, it didn't seem to have existed.

Even so, I thought I would stay where I was until the sea calmed. So it was Sunday morning, August 28, before I left

191

Shroud Cay. There was a gentle breeze blowing. The air smelled clean and fresh-washed. The sky was baby blue. The sea held scarcely a ripple. The whole thing had that amazingly innocent look that nature can take right after a terrible storm —a sort of "Who? Me? Everybody-knows-I'd-never-cause-any-trouble" expression. Even the dinghy towed peacefully in her place.

My main concern now was to get a message to Viola. I had left Nassau on the nineteenth and my last letter to her had been dated the day before. She would know from it that I had been somewhere in the hurricane's path—and she would know that if I was alive I would get a message to her as soon as possible. But the nearest radio station was in George Town, still miles ahead of me. The nearest settlement where I might hope for a mailboat was Black Point, and I headed there.

The wind was light and dead ahead. The motor seemed to feel it had done its duty in the storm. Now it would run a few minutes and cut off. Dirty gasoline was clogging the line. Each time this happened I had to crawl on my belly over life preservers, old buckets, and various odds and ends to reach the tank under the stern deck. I would take the rubber tube from my stethoscope with me, slip it over the gas outlet, and blow. A rush of air would bubble up through the gas, temporarily clearing away the sludge. And I still had no cutoff valve at the bottom of the tank, so when I removed my finger from the outlet the gas rushed out while I tried frantically to screw the line back into place.

Despite my best efforts I was three days covering the approximately forty miles to Black Point settlement. Finally I made it, coming into harbor just after dark, August 30. Near the end of the dock was a large boat ablaze with electric lights. I hailed a man sculling past in a dinghy and asked what boat it was.

"Dot the mailboat. She leavin' to go into Nassau."

"I've got to get a letter on her!"

"The mailbag done close. I was just there." Then he added,

"The cap'n might take it for you. He very obligin'. He a white man from Abaco."

At that point anybody from Abaco sounded like a long-lost brother. I dashed into my cabin, scrawled a note addressed to Viola that read: "Self and boat safe in Exuma Cays. Love, Evans." I stuffed it in an envelope with money enough to pay for its being sent by radio, addressed that envelope to the Telecommunications Department in Nassau, and jumped into my dinghy.

The mailboat was obviously preparing to sail, but there was still a circle of people on the dock alongside. In the middle of the circle a man squatted, a notebook on his knee, a pencil in his right hand. A flashlight under his left arm directed its beam down on the notebook. I heard someone address him as "Captain," and I asked, "Are you from Abaco?"

"That's right." He did not look up.

"My wife is a native of Marsh Harbour. I wonder if you might know her. Viola Sawyer."

The beam of light slashed up at my face. "My God! Dr. Cottman! Where did you come from?"

It was Leslie Albury of Man-o'-War Cay, whose family I had often treated. Hurriedly I told him of my hurricane experience and asked if he would post my letter to the telecommunications in Nassau.

"I'll do better than that, Doctor. I'll take it to them personally. And tomorrow morning at 8 when the ships in this area are on the air, I'll broadcast your whereabouts. Someone in Marsh Harbour might pick it up."

So next morning at 8 I switched on the *Green Cross*'s radio and heard Captain Albury pass the word of my safe arrival at Black Point. Later I would learn that the broadcast was also heard by Captain Milton Sweeting, another of my seafaring friends who happened to be at that moment in Man-o'-War Cay. He had immediately sailed over to Marsh Harbour to deliver the message to Viola—and had arrived at almost exactly the same time the telegram was delivered.

With my message sent, I stayed on in Black Point for several days. The settlement had been hard hit by the storm. Many of its small frame houses had been destroyed; others had a wall caved in or roof blown away. A small, poverty-stricken settlement at best, Black Point was now well-nigh destitute. So much of the local food supply had been destroyed that many persons faced actual starvation.

In the placid weather following the storm the settlement was infested with hordes of mosquitoes and sand flies. In front of the open door of every hut (there were, of course, no screens) sat a smudge pot. These emitted clouds of acrid smoke supposed to drive away "de varmints." This did not seem to have much effect on the varmints, but it turned the whites of the people's eyes blood-colored. And in the early darkness the little fires, the great clouds of smoke rising in front of each shack, filling the street, drifting in and out of the screenless windows, gave the whole place an eerie, infernolike appearance.

From Black Point I moved on to Farmers Cay, only ten miles away. Now there were reports of another hurricane. It did not appear to be coming my way; but since I had a good anchorage I stayed in it. I had lived through my Shroud Cay experience and, quite honestly, though there were terrifying moments, I had come through with the feeling that I could handle a rough situation. But not so much that I wanted another.

There was plenty of work at Farmers Cay; the people were plagued with gas and wombs trouble as usual. But one case caught me by surprise. This was a solemn-looking young woman who came aboard and sat down with her hands folded. "Doctuh," she said soberly, "I can't seem to get no children. No matter how I tries, I just don't get children. I want you should help me."

I began to question her. Her "health" was regular; she had no physical irregularities that she knew of. I asked about her husband.

She looked surprised. "Oh, Doctuh, I ain' got no husband. I ain' never marry. But all dese other girls around here, they

194

ain' never marry and they havin' children all the time! Can't you help me?"

I said I was afraid there was nothing I personally could do.

The hurricane I was watching passed safely out of the area and I moved on to Darby Island, then to Moss Town, a settlement on the south side of Great Exuma Island. The harbor here is reached by a particularly narrow and crooked creek which I nosed through with great care at high tide. When finally I reached the dock I was greeted with considerable surprise. I was the doctuh? They had heard I was coming. (That wonderful grapevine of the Bahamas!) But who had piloted me up the creek?

I said I had come alone.

This brought more looks of surprise. One of the men turned to the others. "Dot one wonderful mon!" he said. "He carry dis big boat up dis creek, him one, and manage better'n plenty peoples live here all dey life."

A murmur of admiration ran through the crowd. And I am frank to admit my chest swelled a little. What I deeply regretted was that none of my Marsh Harbour friends was present to hear that speech.

24

My Demon Dinghy

Moss town is only eight miles by land from George Town, which is on the north side of Great Exuma. I had told the Nassau post office to forward my mail to George Town, so now I took my bicycle and rode over. That is, I rode where the road was not too rough or the hillside too steep, which was about half the way.

So I was pushing my bicycle when I crested one of the hills and got my first view of George Town. Below me the island sloped steeply, green and lush, to a doll's town of tiny houses. Beyond this lay a sheet of turquoise water, as beautiful as any I have ever seen or hope to see. A half mile across this was Stocking Island, a tall white beacon rising like a spire from its top.

There were quite a few letters. I read some of them while I peddled and pushed back across the island. But the others had to be put off because already there was a crowd waiting for me on the dock and I had to go to work.

I was four days in Moss Town, then moved on to The Ferry, a settlement on the Little Exuma side of the narrow cut that separates Great Exuma Island from Little Exuma. There I dressed and went ashore, inquiring for one Mr. Gerald Fitzgerald, whom Mr. Turtle had recommended I see. Gerald Fitzgerald turned out to be a grasshopper-spry, wiry, leathery-skinned, seventy-five-year-old Englishman. He had come to the Bahamas when he was fifteen and had lived here ever since. To judge by the plans he was making for the future, he expected to be here another sixty years.

Perhaps my expression showed I was silently adding figures, for he began to laugh. "The Fitzgeralds are noted for longevity," he told me. "You see the old lady on the wall? That's my great-aunt."

It was a striking portrait of a dark-haired, stern-faced lady who appeared to be about sixty or sixty-five years old and well preserved. "She was something past one hundred when that was painted," Mr. Fitzgerald said. "She lived to be one hundred and twenty, the oldest age ever officially recorded in England. I don't know how long she might have lived; she was in the best of health; but she climbed a pear tree one day after the fruit, a limb broke, and she fell out." Mr. Fitzgerald laughed. "When I get to be a hundred and twenty, I hope I'll still be picking pears. But I'll do it from the ground."

Rolle Town is a little settlement only a few miles from The Ferry, and of all the places I have ever been in the Bahamas

196

these two are among my favorites. There is a genuinely friendly, happy attitude about them. My first evening in Rolle Town will illustrate.

I was invited, before I had been in town an hour, to attend a musical entertainment at the church. Apparently everybody was there, and all in excellent humor. Everybody laughed and talked with everybody else, and as a stranger I was made to feel completely at home and welcome. A big choir sang spirituals (the American spiritual, often in a local adaptation, is very popular with the Bahamian natives) and sang them extremely well. Afterward I was asked as a "distinguished visitor" (any visitor in Rolle Town would be distinguished; but I was also "de doctuh") to say a few words. I asked how many in the audience had heard a Sunday-morning radio program, popular at that time, called "Roll Jordan." The response was unanimous. "Well," I said, "from the singing here tonight I would say that Rolle Town was every bit as good as Roll Jordan."

This brought on loud applause and much good-humored cheering.

I had been at Rolle Town several days when, early one morning, I got a message from Mr. Lewis Fitzgerald, back at The Ferry. Lewis was old Mr. Gerald Fitzgerald's nephew, a ship carpenter, a rugged, friendly, powerfully built man of about forty. Like his uncle, he had gone out of his way to make my brief stay at The Ferry comfortable. Now, the messenger said, he had suddenly become ill, running a high fever and suffering terribly with a pain in his shoulder.

I would have left immediately, but even before I could get my sails up the Bahama grapevine had spread the word I was leaving. This brought the usual burst of patients who simply had to "get sound" before I departed. Consequently it was noon before I got away. The wind and tide were against me and it was nearly dark before I dropped anchor at The Ferry.

There had been no chance to eat lunch before leaving Rolle Town, and no chance to eat on the way. I hesitated, but decided I'd best put off dinner until I had seen Lewis. So I went ashore, and found a man with a jeep on the dock waiting for me. He had a letter from Mr. Felix Deleveaux, the teacher at Moss Town, saying his wife was very ill, in great pain, and would I please come at once.

I told the driver to wait until I had seen Lewis. He was in bed. His temperature was 104; his shoulder was swollen with fluid and needed to be aspirated. But the only light was a lamp. It was not a good one and I simply didn't dare try this in the semidarkness. So I did what I could to make him comfortable for the night, then took the jeep to Moss Town. It was a drive of twenty-two miles over a road that nothing but a jeep could have crossed, and well after midnight when I arrived.

Judging from Mr. Deleveaux's letter, I had thought the trouble must be an obstruction of the bladder or urethra; so I took along a catheter and, in case that failed, a special cannula and trocar for suprapubic puncture. But, as often happened, I had got the wrong impression from a letter. It was not a case of obstruction but of renal failure. There was no distension and catheterization yielded little result. The pain seemed to be centered in the left ovary. I had brought no diuretics; however, the mailboat was to leave for Nassau within a few hours. So I did what I could to make her comfortable on the trip and wrote a letter for her to take to the hospital.

By now it was the small hours of the morning. I got a little sleep. At 7 the jeep came for me and we headed back toward The Ferry. On the way I ate a box of lemon snaps and a small tin of cream, which I had been thoughtful enough to pack with my medicine before leaving the *Green Cross*.

Back at Lewis Fitzgerald's I found his condition had deteriorated seriously and rapidly. His temperature was now 105. Now there were two swellings, one on his shoulder and the other on the side of his chest. I believed they were pus pockets and would have to be drained. But what if I were wrong? Also, I had never made a puncture into the chest cavity and naturally I was apprehensive.

But what if I didn't operate?

The ideal course would be to get him immediately to the hospital in Nassau. But the nearest wireless station was in

George Town and it operated only at certain hours of the day. If I did get a message through, a plane might or might not be sent immediately. (I thought of Luther Bain's daughter waiting for the plane on Crooked Island.) And if the plane did come, could it land here at The Ferry? I didn't know and no one else seemed to know. If it landed at George Town, how were we going to move Lewis over those horrible roads?

Adding it all up, I realized that the best we could hope for was to get Lewis to the hospital in twenty-four hours. But there was the question—could he wait that long? Obviously the infection was spreading rapidly. His temperature was increasing and already he was lapsing into periods of semiconsciousness. I was afraid a complete collapse was imminent.

I called Mrs. Fitzgerald aside and told her the entire situation as best I could. She listened, stood for a moment with her head bowed, then said, "Go ahead, Doctor. I know you will do everything possible."

"I'll need help." Lewis's fourteen-year-old son was there and I turned to him. "Can you help me?"

"Yes, sir."

We went to work. The area around the swellings was extremely sensitive and I had to infiltrate heavily with novocaine. I used a cannula, which is a small metal tube, and a trocar— a small stylet with a sharp point that can be worked inside the cannula. This had to be forced into the pus pocket through an incision. It wasn't easy, and I had trouble locating the exact position of the pocket. Finally I felt the trocar enter the pocket and I removed it, leaving the cannula to serve as a drainage tube. From this suddenly shot out a stream of bloody pus.

"Wipe that away, gently," I told Lewis's son.

There was no answer. I looked around and saw him stretched on the floor in a dead faint.

I couldn't leave Lewis to revive the boy. And I was afraid that if I called Mrs. Fitzgerald and she came in and found her son looking as if he were dead, she might well pass out beside him. On the other hand, I had to have help.

I took a chance and called her, and immediately I knew

199

there was no reason for misgivings. She poured water in her son's face, then quickly realized he was too shaky to be of use and turned to me. "Tell me what you want, Doctor. I'll do it."

She proved to be an excellent nurse. When the first pocket was drained, the second still had to be opened. Through it all she worked steadily. She helped me give Lewis hot Epsom salts fomentations. I infiltrated the spot with more novocaine, and gave him a penicillin injection. He had suffered terribly despite the novocaine; but eventually relief came and he dropped off to sleep.

It was then Mrs. Fitzgerald looked at me. "Doctor," she said, "if when you left here last night you went to Moss Town, and came back from there this morning, when did you last eat?"

I told her I had eaten a box of lemon snaps for breakfast.

"Sit down," she said. And in a very short time she served me a chicken dinner. There is little need to add that I appreciated it.

One day shortly before I left Rolle Town I happened to pass an old woman with a basket of sugar apples—a fruit that looks surprisingly like the bulb of an Easter lily and tastes like its name—a sweet apple. When I asked if they were for sale, she said she would be happy to give me all I wanted. I insisted on paying, but she merely laughed. "Dey grow wild, Doctuh. Dey free to anybody raise de hand to pick dem."

I had occasion to remember this a few days later when I took the *Green Cross* into George Town. The first patients who came aboard were alternately wheedling and sullen. When I went ashore I was immediately besieged by a crowd of children begging for "t'rupence." When I asked directions, I was asked if I wanted a professional guide; when I said no, my request for simple directions was ignored. And when I wanted to buy sugar apples I was charged a shilling apiece for them.

The attitude was similar and yet different from that I had encountered on Mangrove Cay at Andros. Mangrove Cay is close to the center of government in Nassau. At George Town

200

the United States had for a number of years maintained a naval base. Money had flowed freely, but not always with resulting good will. Many of the naval personnel regarded the natives as thoroughly spoiled, while the natives usually looked on the sailors as outlanders who owed them money just for being there. I had a chance to discuss this with an Englishman who had been there during the war and in the conversation I mentioned that at Moss Town I had been charged threepence for a sugar apple, at Rolle Town they had been given to me, while in George Town, where they were equally plentiful, I was charged a shilling.

"I know," he said. "When your sailors first came here the natives frequently gave them sugar apples. If they did sell them, they charged a penny. But you know how open-handed Americans are. To your sailors a penny didn't seem like anything. If a native asked a penny for a sugar apple, the sailor usually gave him threepence, maybe more. Well, it didn't take the natives long to decide that if your sailors were paying three and four times the price asked for something, then it must actually be worth far more. So they began to ask a shilling, and then two shillings. The sailors got mad and refused to pay. That made the natives mad. And what began as a simple act of American generosity—or lavishness, if you prefer—wound up causing a great deal of ill will on both sides. I once saw the same thing happen in Brazil, and probably it happened in ports all over the world." He shook his head. "What it proves, I suppose, is that where you Americans are more free with your money than your long-range understanding, you can do more harm than good, and sometimes make more enemies than friends."

There was another thing I noticed particularly about George Town. A larger percentage of the people were almost white than in any other place I visited, and far more conscious of it, proud of their white blood while bitterly resenting the mixture. One of my patients told me, "My father was an Englishman—a pure white man. But—" and his mouth twisted in something close to a snarl—"he didn't have any more sense than to marry a damn black woman." It was an attitude that seemed quite common.

My plan was to go no farther south than Hog Cay at the south end of Great Exuma. But from there it was only sixteen miles east to Long Island, where I was told much work would be waiting for me.

I spent a night anchored in Hog Cay Cut. Next morning the wind was dead against me, but I decided I could make it across to the settlement of Simms anyway. I started my engine and went up in the bow to take up my grapnel. It was hooked in coral and I couldn't budge it. So I pulled the boat up directly over the grapnel, made the hawser fast around the Samson post, and gave her the gas. Somewhere below, the grapnel fluke straightened out and let go. I heaved it on deck, and in the same moment noticed that the *Green Cross* was now headed straight for some nearby rocks. I rushed back and threw the engine astern. The boat stopped her forward rush and backed up a few feet. Then the engine made a strange, strangling sound and stopped.

I put the clutch in neutral, pushed the starter, and once more the engine purred. I engaged the clutch. The engine stopped with a horrible choking noise.

I had one of those sinking feelings that I knew where the trouble was—and I did. When I had first put the *Green Cross* in reverse, she had backed into my dinghy and the propeller had become fouled in the painter.

I dropped my big anchor and pondered the matter. Hog Cay Cut was supposed to be a favorite hunting ground of barracuda and shark, for whose company I had little craving. On the other hand, it was impossible to do anything about my fouled propeller from inside the boat. I tried sitting in the dinghy and pulling it up close. I should have known better. The dinghy would buck like a wild horse, then charge head-on into the *Green Cross* as if trying to sink her.

Finally I put on my sea goggles, took a rusty butcher knife (my John S. George & Company machete still had no edge on

202

it), and went over the side. I had hopes of unwinding the painter from the propeller, but that proved utterly futile. Cutting it wasn't much better. I sat straddling the rudder, my chin at water level. The blades of the propeller were turned at such an angle it was impossible to get a clean cut at the rope. The knife was dull. And I was keeping at least one eye and half the other open for barracuda.

Between sawing at the rope and looking out for fish, I forgot the dinghy. That was a mistake and the demon took advantage of it. Mounting on the top of a wave, she suddenly hurled herself at me. I had the knife in my left hand, my right hand pressed against the stern of the *Green Cross*. The bow of the dinghy struck my right index finger just below the nail and flattened it.

The next few moments were blurred. The world turned gray shot with red streaks. I was still sitting astride the rudder and somehow I managed to stay there. I don't remember how. I just realized, after a short while, that I was still there and had to get off. Somehow I slid down into the dinghy, and lay there.

But the propeller was still fouled with the painter, and had to be cleared. So after a few minutes I went back to work. An hour later—it was three and a half hours after I had started work—the propeller was free.

That night I wrote in my diary:

October 7. My right index finger so swollen I can barely circle it with thumb and index finger of my left hand. Three times tonight I have had to get up to soak it in hot Epsom salts solution. I have to grip my pen between thumb and middle finger. If weather is suitable I may try to leave here before daylight, as it will be bright moonlight.

It was a case of "Physician, Heal Thyself" with a vengeance. At that moment I would have much preferred to be sitting in the emergency ward of a good hospital instead of being in a small battered boat, miles from help and with only a few medical books to turn to for a professional consultation.

25

Of a Clinic on the Rocks, and Steventon Hospitality

I LEFT Hog Cay Cut at 3:45 A.M., under a yellow and waning moon. The wind was as squarely against me as it could get, but my gasoline supply was very low. So all day by sail it was beat, beat, beat, back and forth. And all day it was throb, throb, throb in my swollen finger. Between tacks I studied my medical books, with more than usual personal interest, reading everything I had on contusions, especially mashed fingers.

In this case it turned out that as a physician for myself I was not worth the hire. The truth is, there was little I could do except keep the finger in a hot Epsom salts solution as much as possible. That helped, I suppose, but it didn't stop the pain, which went on for several days. And after it did stop, the finger was to remain semi-numb for many years.

It was only sixteen miles to Simms, but with the wind against me I was still four or five miles out as darkness fell. Finally I lowered my sails and started the engine. Ahead a dim light was visible and I steered for it.

It is very difficult, for me, at least, to judge the distance of a light on a dark night. This one did not seem to get any closer —until suddenly I realized I was almost on top of it. I threw my engine in reverse, dropped the anchor, and cut off the motor.

"Is that the doctor?" came a voice, surprisingly close.

"Why yes," I said. "How did you know?"

"We were studying your boat with binoculars before it got dark, and saw the green cross on her bow."

It was a Mr. Simms, the local schoolteacher. He was, he said, standing on the public dock (I couldn't see him) and I would be quite safe where I was anchored. Also there were a lot of patients who would be down to see me in the morning.

He was right on all counts. In fact, I had so many patients that for three days I got no farther ashore than the public dock, and might have almost starved if it had not been for the kindness of Mrs. Knowles, the wife of the local storekeeper, and Miss Simms, the postmistress. Both these ladies generously sent me food while I worked, and later had me to dinner several times.

From Simms I worked at other settlements along the north end of Long Island. Also I had the *Green Cross* beached, her bottom scrubbed and painted, her gas tank cleaned, and a screen wire fastened over the end of the fuel line in an effort to baffle my old friend Dirty Gas. Then the first nor'wester of the season came down and for several days I was content to be safely at anchor.

That first nor'wester served to remind me that I had been gone from home for almost four months rather than the "few" weeks originally planned. I had gone as far south as I had figured on going, and maybe a little farther. Also, I was coming into a season of increasingly bad weather, with winds more and more out of the north, making the return home more and more difficult. I decided I had better get about it.

On October 31 I turned and headed for home.

It was one of those wonderful windy days the good Lord might have invented just to make sailing pure pleasure—a day on which, for a change, the wind and I were going in the same direction. I left Simms at 6:30 A.M. and at 10:30 I was passing through Hog Cay Cut—a trip of four hours against sixteen going over. By 3:30 I was anchoring at The Ferry.

Next day was just as lovely, but my rush homeward got interrupted. As I started out of The Ferry Cut a man hailed me from the rocks. He was sick and had walked from Rolle Town to "get sound." The tide was ebbing and I was going in the direction of Rolle Town anyway, though I had not planned to stop there. I took him with me, and when I put him off at the dock I found so many patients waiting, it was two days before I got away.

This time I made it only as far as George Town. Then came another nor'wester that lasted for a solid week. In fact, it was still blowing on the eleventh when finally I sailed up the coast to Steventon. The anchorage there was extremely rough and the constable volunteered to pilot me to a much better one in Ann's Creek, two miles away.

That term "better" was the constable's only. Ann's Creek proved to be a safe anchorage, but about as miserable a one as it was possible to find. The creek was narrow, crooked, and shallow. We stuck several times going up it at high tide. When the tide went out, the *Green Cross* was left firmly aground and canted sharply to starboard—so sharply that if I tried to sleep in the port bunk I rolled out onto the deck. When I tried to sleep in the starboard one, there was that shelf of medical books in my ribs once again. I would have got out of there next morning, except the wind was once more blowing hard out of the northwest and the sea too rough for travel.

Also I had patients. The word had spread that a doctuh done reach Ann's Creek and the people came in flocks. While the tide was high and the *Green Cross* sat on an even keel I used the boat as an office. But as the tide ebbed the *Green Cross* sloped more and more sharply. Patients began to slide off the examining table and it was impossible even to walk on deck without holding on. So with the enthusiastic help of the patients, I moved my "sounding" equipment and tooth-extraction instruments ashore. Along the creek bank there were some big, flat-topped rocks, with a small grove of trees nearby. I set up my clinic on the rocks. When privacy was necessary I would accompany my patient back among the trees and have him or

206

her lie down on a grassy spot for examination. It was all quite idyllic.

I had another night of sleeping wrapped around the bookshelf. It would have been of some help, if not comfort, if I could have absorbed knowledge by osmosis, but it didn't seem to work. By morning I was determined to get out of Ann's Creek on the first high tide.

This came at 2 P.M. But at that time I still had five patients, three women and two men. I told the men if they would help me get out of the creek, I would then sail all five of them back to Steventon, and "sound" them on the way.

It turned out to be a good thing for me. We made it down the creek without too much trouble, but went aground once more on a bar at the entrance. I moved the women into the bow, hoping their weight would trip up the stern a bit. One man carried the anchor forward in the dinghy. The other pulled on the anchor hawser. I ran the engine full speed. And finally we bumped over the bar into clear water.

On the way to Steventon four of my passengers sat in the bow, but one, a buxom black lady whose skin glistened as if it had been recently polished, sat in the stern where I was steering. She chattered away happily and in the course of her chattering asked me, "When you was at Steventon las' week, did you notice one little white boy about seven year old?"

I had noticed a child that age with skin a clear amber color.

"Dot my boy," she said proudly. "I got him by a R.A.F." She paused, looking at me, her expression both concerned and friendly. "Doctuh, don't you get lonesome, you one, goin' about on dis boat?"

She did not wait for an answer, jumping (I suppose) to what she considered an obvious affirmative. "I got a nice daughter, eighteen year old. She love to go wid you on dis boat, and she make you a fine companion. Does you want her to go wid you?"

It was such a totally honest and friendly offer that I didn't know how to answer. Certainly I didn't want to hurt her feelings. "Thank you," I said. "But I—well, you see, the boat only has one comfortable bunk, and—"

"Doctuh, dat's all you'll need."

"Yes, but, well, I've sort of got used to traveling alone. And I'm on my way home. I may not ever get back this way to bring your daughter back. I—"

She shook her head, puzzled at the vagaries of some outlanders.

I dropped my passengers in Steventon, and since the weather reports were good, the sea smooth, I decided to remain overnight. I had heard there was a refrigerator in Steventon and I could buy ice. This was a rare luxury and I decided to go ashore after supper to get some. In preparation I made a pot of tea to drink with the ice.

Just as I was getting ready to go ashore a dinghy came alongside. In it were a young man and a girl—and two trays of ice cubes. "Doctuh," said the young man, "someone tell me you want some ice."

"Indeed I do. Thank you. You've saved me the trip ashore. How much do I owe you?"

He looked pained. "Oh, Doctuh, I ain' bring this ice to sell. I bring it to give you."

"Thank you. Thank you very much. I've made some tea. Won't you come aboard and have some with me?"

He and the girl exchanged glances. "Come on," I said. So they climbed aboard and sat on the port bunk while I poured the tea.

The young man watched me. "Doctuh, you ain' want some rum with this ice? I could go ashore and get you some at the bar."

"No thanks. I don't drink rum."

"I could get you some Scotch whisky."

I shook my head.

"Den you must let me get some beer."

I told him I was a teetotaler, or at least an ice-tea-totaler. He was slow in understanding and I'm not sure he ever did. Obviously he had never before seen anyone use ice without alcohol and the idea was as incomprehensible to him as—well, a man without a woman. "Doctuh," he said (he had come out here to make me a present and he was still trying), "peoples say you been sailin' a long time, you one, on this boat. I got my girl friend with me. She could stay with you tonight and keep you company, if you' say so."

The girl ducked her head and giggled.

"That's very nice of you," I said. "Very generous. But—" Once more I ducked the issue as gracefully as possible.

When they were gone I sat in my cabin and drank more ice tea. Two girls and a bottle of rum had been offered me—quite freely and spontaneously—in one afternoon. Obviously the distinguishing characteristic of Steventon was an excessive generosity. Or perhaps liberality would be a better word.

I decided I had best leave Steventon. I had best get on home in a hurry.

So once more I raised my sails. And once more I ran into trouble. One of my Steventon passengers had told that in passing Sugar Cay I should keep it on my starboard. He should have said port. I went aground at high tide in the middle of the afternoon and was still there next morning when a group of people arrived in a dinghy. They had come out from the settlement of Rolleville (not to be confused with Rolle Town), bringing a very sick young man with them. They needed my help, and considering the situation I was in, I needed theirs.

The young man was sick indeed: suspected tuberculosis complicated with pleurisy, temperature 104, spitting up blood. I started him on sulfa drugs and told them to get him to the hospital at the very first opportunity.

I had not planned to stop at Rolleville, but by the time my new friends had helped me get the *Green Cross* afloat, they had also persuaded me I was needed there. So I went and put in several busy days complicated by another nor'wester that would have kept me in port anyway.

From that point on the weather frequently changed, usually from bad to worse. When I reached Black Point I had an anchorage that was perfectly safe from everything except a southwest wind—so during the night the wind changed to southwest and blew a gale. I had to get out fast, and in order to get out I had to go directly into the teeth of the wind. Yet with my engine running full speed there were moments when I stood still. And worse yet, moments when I actually went backward. In the midst of this my old pal Dirty Gas struck again. The engine stopped.

For the next hour I was actually in more serious danger than I had been at Shroud Cay. I threw the anchor over and I knew that if it didn't hold, if I didn't get the gas line clean in a hurry, if the engine cut off on me again, the *Green Cross* was going to be hurled against the jagged rocks that formed the shore; giant waves would smash it into splinters, and in all probability I would be smashed along with it. But the anchor held and I got the gas line clean. With the engine running again I rounded the point, into open sea and still more mountainous waves.

On my chart Mr. Turtle had marked a creek near a spot called White Horses. It was supposed to be a good anchorage in a southwest wind, and I ran for it, the *Green Cross* climbing up and plunging down the sides of great waves. It made the land itself seem to rise and fall as if caught in an earthquake. When finally I spotted something that looked like the opening into a small cove, I couldn't be sure it was the right place. As I moved closer, the sea and wind were following over my quarter, hurling me ahead like a blown cork. Was the water deep enough? It was a cloudy day with none of the tints by which I could usually tell depths. But I dare not turn back. And then it was too late even to try. I thought I saw the darker green of a channel. And then I thought it wasn't a channel—it was grass on a shallow bottom. By then there was nothing I could do anyway. A great wave charged at me, lifted the stern of the *Green Cross,* flung the boat forward—and I was in calm water with the engine purring quietly and a beautiful little cove around me.

210

That night I wrote:

November 25. This cove opens to the west-northwest and I am protected from every other direction. My chief worry is about food and water. The wretched little stores I have visited in the past few weeks don't keep anything to eat. I had no idea of being so delayed by weather. I have cut myself to half rations now. If only I could get two days of good weather I could be in Nassau.

The next entry read:

November 26, 7 A.M. Last night was a nightmare. All yesterday it was smooth and quiet in here. At 7:15 P.M. I listened to the weather forecast from ZNS and it was for gentle to moderate southwest winds. I went to bed with only the grapnel down.

Four A.M. was awakened by a violent pitching of the boat. On deck I found the wind had increased to a shrieking gale, stronger even than yesterday's. And was now blowing from the west-northwest, directly into this cove. Before I could move, the *Green Cross* was aground and the tide was ebbing.

Breakfast at dawn consisted of a few Ritz crackers and a cup of lime juice. I am on the strictest rations.

The wind is still blowing like fury and I cannot possibly get the *Green Cross* afloat without help. I will have to walk to Black Point for help.

26

Home Is the Sailor,
and Gone Again

About 8:30 I set out. I found a path that left the cove going in the general direction of Black Point. For perhaps two hundred yards it wound through rocks and low, scrubby brush. Then it divided.

I took the one that seemed to go in the right direction. Gradually it dwindled in size and finally disappeared among some rocks. I went back and tried another branch. The same thing happened. I tried another, and another. They all forked and reforked, and all the forks soon faded into nothing.

Well, I knew the general direction of Black Point, so I gave up trying to follow paths and set out through the bushes. I was barefooted—by this time my feet were tougher than most shoes —and wearing a pair of shorts that were not in too good condition when I started. Pushing my way through the bushes didn't help any. I hadn't brought my unsharpened machete, and there were times when I had to break my way through. In other places I crawled on hands and knees.

After two hours of this I suddenly stepped forth into a large cleared space. About a hundred feet from me an old woman, her back to me, was kneeling, planting beans. As I approached I could hear her talking gently to herself, but she did not hear me.

212

Ten feet from her I stopped. "Mawnin', mam," I said. "Could you—?"

The old lady shot straight into the air, still in a kneeling position. Around her, beans rose in a fountain. In mid-air she turned, and came down facing me. She still had her pipe in her mouth, but one look at me and her mouth sagged open and the pipe fell out.

"Jesus!" she cried. It was not an exclamation, but a direct appeal. "Lord Jesus, save me!" she screamed, and departed with a speed that, considering her age, was totally amazing.

"Wait!" I shouted after her. "Wait! Come back! I want to ask you something."

She must have decided my voice emanated from flesh and blood rather than the spirit world, for at the edge of the field she paused and looked back. "Who you? Where you come from?"

"I'm the doctor. I have a boat, the *Green Cross*, in a cove back over there."

It helps to be famous; it helps to be a big frog in a small pond at times. She had heard of the doctor and the *Green Cross*, and he was likely to show up anywhere, even to fall from the heavens into the middle of a field. "I t'ought you was a spirit," she said, still shaky. And then directed me how to reach Black Point.

In the settlement I found a man who agreed to come out and help me. I had less success finding food. The only thing I managed to buy was a pound of sugar. With that under my arm, my helper and I headed back for the cove.

The path we followed was more circuitous than the route I had taken, but it was a path. And as we walked along the north side of the island I was given a wonderful demonstration of the power and might and beauty of the ocean. The cove I had entered was near a spot on the chart marked "White Horses," but what White Horses was, I had no idea. It was not a settlement. Now I could see a promontory ahead of us, and against this tremendous waves were crashing one after another

213

with a continuous, thundering roar. The earth quivered with the impact; spray shot skyward and hung in clouds. Then we rounded the promontory. And right in front of us, carved by the sea in marble-white rock, were the heads and breasts of two magnificent horses. As each wave crashed against them and receded, they seemed to be emerging from the sea, bursting from it in a furious chariot race where Neptune himself might have been the driver.

When we reached the *Green Cross* the tide was high. We got the boat into deep water and safely anchored. I took my helper ashore, then sculled back, against the wind this time. It was 2 P.M. I lay down and rested for an hour, then ate a bowl of corn flakes with tinned milk, four Ritz crackers, and a cup of lime juice, my dinner ration.

No night lasts forever and any wind blows itself out. November 27, with a calm sea and a light breeze, I was on my way again. I anchored one night at Bell Island, another at Shroud Cay, where conditions were far better than on my previous visit. Except for food, that is. I was getting sick of Ritz crackers and lime juice. At 5 P.M. on the twenty-ninth I tied up at Mr. Turtle's dock in Nassau, went ashore, ate two steaks, and drank a quart of fresh milk.

At Nassau there was more bad weather. When I did leave, heading for Sandy Point on Abaco, the winds were still against me and the sea rough; but by using the engine the whole way I covered the sixty-three miles in seventeen and three-quarter hours. Unfortunately, this proved too much for the engine. Next morning when I went to start it, it simply refused. A mechanic from one of the crawfish boats looked it over and found distributor trouble, carburetor trouble, and a burned-out condenser.

The closer a person gets to home, after having been away a long time, the more impatient he becomes and the bigger hurry he is in. Delays that a month or two before would have seemed minor suddenly become unbearable. At least that is the way it was with me. Now that I was on Abaco and within a relatively few miles of home, I simply had no time to fiddle around wait-

214

ing for the *Green Cross*'s engine to be repaired. I took passage on the *Crustacean,* another crawfish boat.

But the *Crustacean* was not going to Marsh Harbour. Travel is rarely that simple in the Bahamas. It was going to Woolen Dean, a cay about eight miles southeast of Abaco and about twenty-five miles from Marsh Harbour. There the engineer of the *Crustacean,* a young man named Victor Russell, who also came from Marsh Harbour, and I borrowed a dinghy with an outboard motor. We ran the eight miles across to Abaco, then turned up the coast. Here the water was so shallow we were out of the boat pulling it more than we were in it riding. But finally we reached the Murphy Town landing.

And now at long last there remained only a seven-mile walk across the island to Marsh Harbour, and home.

I got there in the late afternoon. Neither Gayle nor Mother Sawyer was in sight when I opened the door, but Viola was in the kitchen getting dinner. Her back was turned and she did not hear me. I went into the kitchen and put my hand on her shoulder. She turned, expecting to see her mother or one of her relatives. Her eyes widened, her lips parted slightly. "I'm home," I said, and for a while there was no need for other conversation.

When Viola did speak she was holding me at arm's length and shaking her head. "Oh, Evans," she said. "You look terrible."

I suppose I did. I was dirty. My hair was matted from sea water and wind. I was twenty pounds lighter than when I left home. But it didn't seem to matter too much to Viola at the moment. Gayle, however, was another matter.

Her mother brought her into the room in her arms. "Look, Gayle," she said. "This is Daddy."

Gayle looked, and did not seem to care for what she saw. She turned her head away. Viola tried again, "This is Daddy, darling. He's come home."

Gayle put her face against her mother's shoulder.

"Don't you want to kiss your daddy?"

She looked at me then, carefully, from toe to head. "No,"

215

she said. "No." Suddenly she wriggled out of her mother's arms and crossed the room and climbed into a chair. There was a picture of me on the wall and she patted it. "Daddy," she said happily. "Daddy, Daddy. Gone in boat."

But I wasn't gone in a boat now and I watched her, caught in the conflicting emotions that must have tortured the home-coming fathers of small children since the first man went to sea: yearning to touch her, to be accepted and loved by her, and at the same time afraid of frightening her and delaying the moment of acceptance.

Things settled down in the next few weeks. Even Gayle came to accept me, gradually. I was kept busy in Marsh Harbour and the neighboring settlements. From Dr. Stratton I bought eighteen acres of land fronting on the bay and including a bluff higher even than Gun Bluff. The view was superb but unfortunately there was no way to get there. I bought a large crate of dynamite and set out to blast a road up the bluff, a process that shook Marsh Harbour to its foundations.

While I was working on this road I had several patients from the south shore of Grand Bahama Island visit me. Dr. Gottlieb, they said, was still at Pine Ridge on the north side, but transportation was so difficult and he was so busy with his lumber company work, he was rarely able to visit the south shore. The patients who came to me in Marsh Harbour all asked if it would be possible for me to make a tour of the south-shore settlements. A doctor was badly needed.

I wrote Dr. Gottlieb about the matter, and got a very prompt and cordial answer. He would be very glad indeed if I could make a trip along the south shore since it was extremely difficult for him to get there.

So in November 1951 I set out.

There was no way to make the trip in the *Green Cross*. The south shore of the Grand Bahama was practically without harbors. Open to the full fury of the ocean, it had the reputation of being one of the most dangerous places in the Bahamas,

216

especially in winter. Consequently the scattered settlements were isolated and primitive, one of the things that appealed to me about the trip. My plan was to take the mailboat to West End, the settlement at the west end of Grand Bahama. From there I would work my way east by any means available, doctoring as I went. At Sweeting's Cay, at the east end of the island, I would catch the *Crustacean,* which stopped there now and then to buy crawfish, and go with it to West Palm Beach, where the crawfish were sold, then back to Abaco.

It was a very neat plan and would give me a chance to do some Christmas shopping in the States and be home for the holidays.

I should have known better.

I had to go to Nassau to catch the mailboat for West End. The weather was bad. By the time I reached Nassau the boat had been gone for two days. So instead of waiting another week, I changed plans and took the *Richard Campbell* to Sweeting's Cay.

There was no harbor. We anchored a half mile off the creek mouth and a dinghy was put over, loaded with sacks of flour, grits, and rice. The wind was blowing, the water rough, the dinghy pitching. "We'll take your things ashore next trip, Doctor," the captain told me.

From the looks of that dinghy I was just as glad to wait—and lucky too. It hadn't gone fifty feet when a wave struck it broadside, swamped it, and washed two of the crew overboard. Another dinghy recued them and towed the swamped one back to the *Richard Campbell.* There it was bailed out and my twenty-five cardboard boxes of drugs and food were put aboard.

We too made just about fifty feet. Then a wave came over the bow, half filling the boat. We didn't sink; we just started to settle slowly. My cardboard boxes started to disintegrate, not so slowly. So we headed back for the *Richard Campbell,* and barely made it in time.

The cook gave me some new boxes for my gear. This time

we covered them with a tarpaulin, fastening it to the gunwales so that most of the water that came over us was shed back into the sea. And just before dark I was put ashore at Sweeting's Cay.

27

Changing Times at Grand Bahama

ANOTHER dinghy from the *Richard Campbell* had already made it ashore and spread the word that the doctuh done reach. As I put foot on land I was greeted by a tall, spare, mulatto gentleman whom I had met several times in Marsh Harbour, and who had pleaded with me to visit Sweeting's Cay. His name was T. Duncombe and he had already rounded up a crowd of boys to carry my belongings. I would, he insisted, stay at his house. The word of my arrival was rapidly spreading and there would be a crowd of patients waiting for me early in the morning. Because of this, Duncombe urged that I unpack and get things ready tonight.

I was hungry, so I started by unpacking my food. Duncombe eyed the strange assortment curiously. There were corn flakes, puffed wheat, sliced bread, butter, jelly, cheese, miscellaneous canned goods. T. Duncombe shook his head sympathetically. "Doctuh," he said, "if I had to eat dem kind of things, I'd starve."

I glanced over to his stove where a pot of hard grits was boiling. "If I had to live on that," I said, also sympathetically, "I would starve."

It took me several hours to unpack and it was after mid-

218

night before I got to bed. It seemed to me I had scarcely lain down when I was startled by a loud voice that for one wild moment I thought came from under my bed. Then I realized it was from beyond the thin partition which separated my room from that of Duncombe and his wife. "Oh Lord!" It was Duncombe's voice. "Oh Lord, how we do thank you, Lord, for dot precious founting of blood which cleanse and sanctify our souls!" His voice rose; it got faster; it had a passionate fervor to it. "And we pray, Lord, we do pray, dot You keep right on sanctifying them. We is sinners, Lord. We is all sinners. But You can make us pure!"

This went on for five minutes. I looked at my watch and it was just after 5 o'clock, not yet daylight. I wondered if Duncombe always got up this early. But just at this point his voice stopped. Two minutes later he was snoring.

I couldn't go back to sleep so I got up and started to fix breakfast. This was a good thing because with the first streaks of daylight, even before I had eaten, patients began to arrive. In his bedroom T. Duncombe kept snoring while his front room filled with patients. They sat on the floor. They brought boxes and sat on them. They lined up on the porch.

This was a Sunday and some of the men told me it was the only day they could see me because the rest of the week they were gone crawfishing. Consequently I announced to the waiting crowd that I had decided to take care of the men today, and the women should come back on Monday. Instantly there arose loud cries of dismay. Some of the women were seriously ill. Some had traveled a long way to get here and could not come back again. So eventually I agreed. If they wanted to wait, I would get to them all as soon as I could.

Obviously no doctor had been to Sweeting's Cay for a long, long time. There was not only a great accumulation of work, but an unusually large proportion of really serious cases. There were internal tumors and other growths that had to be sent to the hospital for major operations, cases of suspected tuberculosis that had to be sent for X-ray. There were several cases of serious heart trouble and two were in advanced stages of dropsy. I worked all day without stopping for lunch. I didn't stop for supper. It was 2 A.M. when the last patient went out the door and I stumbled wearily into my room.

Duncombe and his wife had long since retired. I was too exhausted to cook, but I punched holes in a can of evaporated milk and used it to wash down a few swallows of bread and cheese. Then I lay back on the bed, meaning simply to rest a few moments before I took off my clothes.

"Oh-h Lord!" It was Duncombe's voice, already rising in pitch, going fast and getting faster. "How we thank you, Lord, for dot precious founting of blood which cleanse our souls." It was the same prayer as well as I could make out, the words coming in a torrent, rising higher and higher until they broke for lack of breath.

I looked at my watch. Once more it was a few minutes after 5. And once more Duncombe's prayers soon lapsed into silence, to be followed quickly by snores. It was a routine that never varied during my visit to Sweeting's Cay, and though it played havoc with my sleep, at least it had me up and waiting for patients.

These continued to pour in, though there were no more days as rushed as that first Sunday. One thing, however, worried me. My plan (the revised one) had been to board the first crawfish boat that put into Sweeting's Cay and use its radio to contact Viola's brother Charles, who was now captain of the *Crustacean*, and arrange a rendezvous somewhere along the Grand Bahama coast. But time went on and no crawfish boat came to Sweeting's Cay.

Eventually I decided that if no radio would come to me, then I must go to it. According to Duncombe, the closest radio telephone was at Gold Rock Creek, some thirty-three miles to the west. Here the United States had established a missile-tracking base. Duncombe would take me in his dinghy as far as High Rocks, twenty-six miles from Sweeting's Cay. From there I could reach Gold Rock Creek by road.

We set out, accompanied by Duncombe's son, early Saturday morning. I took with me three satchels containing my general medical equipment, tooth-extraction instruments, and a few commonly used drugs.

The wind was from the north, off the land. We were going west so we made good time over a smooth sea. As we proceeded, Duncombe entertained me with vivid accounts of all the wrecks and drownings that had occurred in these waters. "You see dot place, Doctuh? Dot Black Point, one bad place. Last winter a dinghy just like this one turn over right where we is now and everybody got lost. Four mens and one woman with a baby. One of the mens float up on the beach, but when they find him the crows done pick his eyes out. And they find the baby's head, but the shark carry off all the rest."

"That was last winter?"

"Just about this time, Doctuh. And you see dot big rock up yonder? One time a boatload of children run onto it. They all drown. All of them. Now you see over dere? Dot's where——"

It was a coast of calamities and Duncombe told of them in loving detail. While he talked the morning passed. Also the wind increased and backed to the northwest, slowing our progress. More and more coral shoals began to show up around us —practically everyone with its story of disaster. Duncombe's son, standing in the bow, was constantly shouting warnings to his father at the tiller. The sea got rougher. All around us it foamed and frothed at coral fangs.

Finally Duncombe said, "Doctuh, I can't make it no more. Just round this next point is one small missile station. It belong to the base at Gold Rock and dere is a road to it. I goin' to put you ashore here and turn back."

It was a suggestion I agreed with completely—until we rounded the point and I saw what lay between us and land. The water was so thick with coral shoals there seemed no way through them. But somehow Duncombe got through. He let me off in thigh-deep water and I waded ashore carrying my three satchels.

I was met by three young men in uniform. They did not smile and their faces were not friendly. Behind them was a small outpost of the Gold Rock base, one tiny shack and some

221

curious-looking instruments. These three men (as I would learn later) made up the total complement, and they were not accustomed to visitors wading in from the open sea.

"What do you want here?" one of them barked.

"I am trying to get to High Rocks," I said. "But the weather got rough and I couldn't go any farther in the boat. I believe there is a road from here?"

The men looked at one another. "He speaks English," one of them said.

"You don't think they'd send somebody didn't speak anything but Russian," another one said.

I started to take my things out of the dinghy and carry them ashore.

"What's all that stuff?" asked one of the men suspiciously.

"That's my medical equipment," I answered.

"You mean you're a doctor?"

"That's right."

"Well, I'll be! A doctor drops in out of nowhere!"

Both the sea and the situation were making Duncombe uncomfortable. He shoved off just as soon as I got my things out of his boat.

"O.K., Doc, we'll help you with your—uh—medical equipment." The way the soldier said it made it clear he thought I was lying. "But don't try to come any closer."

I felt I should try to convince them I was on the level, so I said, "Just let me look inside that satchel a moment to see whether any of my things got wet." Opening up the satchel, I took out my sounding rod, blood pressure instruments, elastic bandage. They gathered around and inspected the instruments and empty bags. Meanwhile I did my best to explain the situation.

"O.K.," one of them said finally. "There's a truck right up there. It'll be going into High Rocks in an hour or so. Put your bags in that and wait."

I did. The young men moved off about their work, keeping still-suspicious eyes on me. Then the truck driver arrived and took me into High Rocks, which was as far as he was going.

But he did introduce me to the local schoolteacher, a Mr. Wildgoose; and Mr. Wildgoose immediately asked if I would stay overnight at his home. There were a great many persons, he said, who would like to take advantage of my visit.

This was about noon, when Mr. Wildgoose was home for lunch. He said he would tell the schoolchildren that afternoon about my arrival, and they could spread the word when school let out at 3. The way I figured, the first patients should then begin to arrive about 4. I decided to use the interval to walk along the beach, find a quiet, shady spot, and rest awhile.

I found the secluded spot and lay down. But almost immediately, as though in a dream, I heard a faint, familiar sound. "Doctuh," a woman's voice was calling. "Oh, Doctuh."

I turned over and put my face in the sand, my eyes tight closed. I was almost asleep. "Doctuh!" the voice called. It was closer now. But I was hidden by bushes. I lay still.

The bushes parted and a little old woman pushed through. "Dere you is, Doctuh. I most thought I was going to lose you."

I sat up wearily. "How did you find me?"

"Why, I just follow your feet prints."

"But there were all kinds of prints all over the beach," I said. "And I was barefoot, like everybody else. How did you know which were mine?"

"Why, Doctuh, dot was easy. All de others were colored peoples' feet."

Well, I had read that Indians could tell one tribe from another by the prints of their moccasins, but I had never expected to have such skill used on me. I asked what was wanted with me, now I was found.

"Dere is plenty peoples to de teacher's house waitin' on you. Dey want to get sound."

Once more I had failed to take into account the magic of the Bahamian grapevine. School would not be out for an hour yet; but when I returned to Mr. Wildgoose's home there were already a dozen patients and more arriving. Once more I went to work. Since I had only a few drugs with me, there were many cases where I had to write down the patient's name,

223

along with the prescription, and promise to send the medicine back from Sweeting's Cay when I returned there.

I worked until well after midnight, then had to get up at daylight to catch a ride, this time with one of my patients, into Gold Rock Creek.

The missile base there proved to be quite a sizable outfit with handsome buildings and well-kept lawns, and around them fantastic, towering instruments that looked like something from Mars. The officer in charge of the radio station, when I located it, was sympathetic. "But we operate on a completely different set of frequencies from the local boats," he told me. "The only place on Grand Bahama where you can contact your boat is Pine Ridge."

That was twenty-five miles away, on the north side of the island. Fortunately, however, this was a Sunday morning; at 9 a bus would leave to carry soldiers to the Pine Ridge church and I could ride with them. Meanwhile I had an hour to kill.

I was standing in the sunlight, watching soldiers wander aimlessly back and forth, when I heard a piano. Someone was playing Paderewski's Minuet, the music seeming almost as strange, as out of place here on the south shore of Grand Bahama as the base itself and the weird steel towers that rose against the sky all around. Instinctively I followed the sound. There was a large recreation hall in which soldiers stood about in groups, playing games or talking or reading. The piano was against the far wall, surrounded by a group of about twenty men. As I moved closer I saw the pianist was a young soldier. He finished the minuet, was heartily applauded, and started on the Moonlight Sonata.

Quite unconsciously I kept getting closer. Members of the listening group came and went. By the time the player stopped, I was standing close behind him. He turned as if to get up and I said, "Please. Do you play the next movements?"

"Not without my music." He looked at me. "Can you?"

"I could at one time. But it's been a long while since I touched a piano. By now my fingers would be all thumbs."

"Then you need practice." He stood up.

224

I wanted to play. I felt a downright hunger for it. At the same time I knew I would be poor after so long, and I was embarrassed. I have never liked to do in public what I can't do well. But now the audience was good-naturedly urging me on. When I held back someone behind me said, "I think he's a fourflusher. I don't think he knows one note from another."

That settled it. I sat down and struck the first three notes that form the theme for Rachmaninoff's Prelude in C-sharp Minor. "Well!" somebody said. After that I played for my own pleasure, and I hope for that of the soldiers. I was rusty, but I did better than I expected. I was still playing when I looked at my watch and saw it was 8:55 and time for the bus.

At Pine Ridge I located the company launch and over its radio managed to contact Charles on the *Crustacean*. He was, he said, at Red Shank Cay and would be leaving for West Palm Beach early Wednesday morning. "I'll pass Sweeting's Cay creek on the way," he said. "Be out there in a dinghy at 7 A.M., and I'll take you aboard."

With those plans made and nothing to do until the bus returned to Gold Rock Creek, I called on Dr. Gottlieb. He was extremely cordial; both he and Mrs. Gottlieb insisted I stay for dinner, and after my rations of the past week I don't think they had much trouble persuading me. Afterward he showed me the clinic and the changes that had been made since I was there.

"I've been here almost three years with no vacation," he told me. "So this summer I'm entitled to three months, and I want to spend them in Germany. Would you take over for me?"

The offer surprised me. I reminded him I was not an M.D.

"I know," he said. "But the government has seen fit to license you year after year. And you are acquainted with the work here. Most of the people already know and like you."

So the agreement was tentatively made. Dr. Gottlieb would let me know when his own plans were more definite. We shook hands on it and I took the bus back to Gold Rock Creek and from there caught another ride to High Rocks.

But from there back to Sweeting's Cay was another matter.

225

I asked all the patients who came to Mr. Wildgoose's if they knew of anyone going that way and eventually learned that "Ol' John" might be going in his dinghy next morning. Mr. Wildgoose sent for Ol' John.

He was small and wizened. He had a squint in one eye and all his teeth were missing except for the two upper eyeteeth. These protruded, giving him a fanged look. Between them at frequent intervals tobacco juice would squirt violently. "I be proud to take you, Doc," he said. "My old woman wantin' her medicine bad, an' I bring dot back wid me."

That solved another problem. Since I had brought little medicine with me, for the most part I had been writing down the people's names and the drugs they needed. Now I could send it all back from Sweeting's Cay by Ol' John, if he would agree. He pondered this a moment. "I'll do dot for the peoples, Doc. An' I makes dem pay me t'rupence for each medicine."

Mr. Wildgoose agreed this would be fair enough and the people glad to pay in order to get their medicine promptly.

Ol' John said for me to be at his house at 7 next morning. Then as he was about to leave he stopped and looked back. "Is you use to fas' sailin', Doc?"

I told him I was in a hurry to reach Sweeting's Cay and would not mind a little speed.

He gave a high, cackling laugh. "Dot's fine, Doc, 'cause I is a fas' sailer."

The next morning was raw with a hard wind blowing out of the northwest. But since this was off the land I figured the sea would be calm and we should make good time. Carrying my satchels I walked down to Ol' John's house. There was no sign of life. I went around to the back.

An old woman was dozing on a box by the door. "Mawnin', mam," I said.

She started, nearly falling off the box. "I'm looking for your husband," I said. "Is he home?"

"He home," she said, but she didn't sound happy about it. "He in de bed."

"Is he sick?"

226

"Sick wid too much rum."

I explained he was supposed to carry me to Sweeting's Cay and she nodded, apparently having heard something of the arrangement. "I get him for you."

She went inside. The door was open and I could see Ol' John sprawled fully dressed on the bed. The old woman began to shake him. "Get up!" she cried. "De doctuh waitin' for you."

Ol' John made a moaning noise. "Go 'way, woman."

She quit shaking him. She looked around the room, found an ancient wooden coat hanger on the floor, and picked it up. She went back to the bed, planted her feet firmly, and without another word began to whale away with all her strength. "Quit it!" Ol' John bellowed. He pulled himself into a knot, burying his head like a turtle's. "You killin' me, woman! Quit it!"

She kept swinging. Ol' John staggered out of bed, shielding himself with his arms as best he could and at the same time snatching at the coat hanger and missing. "You ol' drunk fool!" his wife cried. "Keepin' de doctuh waitin'! What wrong wid you?"

He saw me for the first time and his two yellow teeth came out in a slow smile. "Hello, Doc. . . ." The smile faded, replaced by a look of pained thoughtfulness. "What you want, Doc? I done clean forgot."

I had no chance to answer. "You so crazy and drunk wid rum, you ain' know nothin'," his wife screamed. "You promise to take de doctuh to Sweetin' Cay. Now get out dis house!" She gave him a violent push.

He clung to the doorsill. "Honey, I ain' had no breakfas'."

"You so full of rum you ain' need no breakfas'. Get out!"

"I need some bread for my dinner."

She picked up a dry loaf and threw it at him. It hit him on the head and bounced on the floor. "Dere your dinner!" she cried. "Take it an' go!"

Staggering slightly, Ol' John groped for the bread, found it, and put it in his coat pocket. His wife watched, her hands on her hips. "Honey," Ol' John said, "ain' you gonna give me one sweet good-by kiss?"

She raised the coat hanger and made at him. But Ol' John was outside and running. "Le's go, Doc," he called.

I caught up with him a hundred feet down the road. He was swaying slightly as he walked and muttering under his breath. But after a moment he turned to look at me, grinning. "How you like my ol' woman, Doc?"

"She treats you pretty rough, doesn't she?"

"Rough? Dot's jus' her way, Doc. Dot's de sweetest little ol' woman in de world. We been marry fifty year an' we ain' never had no fuss yet. Dot one wonderful woman, Doc."

He meant it. He meant every word of it. Which left me pondering on just what would have had to happen before he considered it a fuss.

We found Ol' John's dinghy pulled up on some rocks. It was only ten feet long and half rotted, with a mast out of all proportion to its length. I looked at it skeptically. The wind was blowing hard and I wouldn't have liked the idea of sailing in this boat even if Ol' John had been sober. On the other hand, I was supposed to meet Charles in less than twenty-four hours, and this was the only way to reach Sweeting's Cay.

We got the dinghy launched and I climbed in. Ol' John was unsteady on his feet; his fingers had trouble untying the halyard, but he seemed happy enough. "Lemme tell you sumpn', Doc. Dis one good boat. You never see a safer boat nowhere. Ain' you t'ink so, Doc?"

I said I hoped so.

"Dot's right," Ol' John said. "An', Doc, you gonna see some sailin' today like you never see befo'. I ain' never fool wid no small sail. Dey too slow. Dey fo' mans what coward. I say, de bigger de sail de safer de boat. Dot right, Doc?"

"It's a theory I never heard expounded before."

But Ol' John was not listening. He had his halyard untied finally. He climbed aboard, reeling a bit, and began to raise his sail. I had never seen such a sail on such a boat. It kept going up and up and up. It looked like something on an America Cup racing yacht that had been masted somehow on a tiny piece of driftwood.

"How big—?"

"Dot t'oity-six-yard canvas, Doc." He gave another heave. The tremendous sail went higher. A sudden gust of wind caught it.

I was sitting in the bow. There was no one at the tiller. With all the weight in the bow the dinghy shot ahead, and down— like a crash-diving submarine. Water poured over the bow. I made a wild jump for the stern with Ol' John at my heels.

He gave forth with a demoniacal cackle. "You ain' scared, Doc? Dot ain' nothin'. Dis one safe boat." His yellow fangs gleamed fiendishly at me. "You take dot can and bail, while I steers."

Water was three inches deep in the bottom of the dinghy and I set to work. Now, with our weight more evenly distributed, we were driving ahead at an almost unbelievable speed, the vast sail stretched taut above us. At the tiller Ol' John began to cackle something I supposed was a song, though whether it was a church hymn or a barroom ballad I could not tell. At least he was doing a superb piece of steering.

Certainly he needed to. In places coral heads broke the water; in others they lay just below the surface. Ol' John knew the exact location of every one, but he seemed to know it more by instinct than by sight because he steered without looking. The dinghy flew madly past and around and above shoals, missing them by inches. Silently I prayed that our luck, our guardian angel, whatever it was steered us (I couldn't believe it was any act of reason on Ol' John's part), would stay with us until he sobered up.

Ol' John reached in his coat pocket. I thought he was after the bread he'd put there. Instead his hand came out holding a bottle of rum. Generously he held it toward me. Instinctively I refused. He shook his head, obviously puzzled at the idea of a man who would refuse a drink while delighted at the prospect of not having to share it. "Dis good rum, Doc." He unscrewed the cap and raised the bottle to his mouth.

At this point fate took a hand. A sudden, violent gust hit us with an impact that all but turned the dinghy over. Water

230

poured over the gunwale like Niagara Falls. Both of us flung ourselves on the upturned, weather side of the boat. And Ol' John's bottle went over the side.

The dinghy righted herself swiftly but water was six inches deep over the floorboards. I began grabbing at my baggage and setting it on the thwarts. Ol' John stood gazing back at our wake. "Doc," he wailed, "I done lose my bottle."

"That's a God's blessing."

"I ain' got no more. I—" His voice broke. Then he cried, "I see it, Doc! It still floatin'! I goin' back!"

"Don't be silly."

He was already hauling in his sheets. "Keep going," I told him, bailing away but watching him with one eye. "That bottle will sink before you can get to it. It'll have salt water in it anyway. You won't be able to drink it."

I might as well have talked to the dead. We began a hard and dangerous beat back toward the bottle. It bobbed on the waves, just the mouth out of water. I kept hoping a wave would slosh over and sink it. But it didn't. Soon it was only thirty feet ahead and a little to port. We were close-hauled, with the sail to starboard. I could see we had considerable drift to starboard and would miss the bottle by about ten feet. Ol' John saw it too, grabbed his oar, and began to scull furiously. Now the boat was headed straight into the wind, the big sail flapping violently and making the boom do a crazy jig. I was still on hands and knees, bailing. Every time I raised my head the boom threatened to knock it off.

Now we were only a few feet from the bottle. Ol' John threw down his oar and leaned far over the gunwale. He still missed it by a foot, by six inches. He stretched. But as his fingers inched closer, the long smooth slope of a big wave came in from the opposite side. It lifted the bottle, pushing it toward Ol' John's hand. It also slopped over into the open mouth of the bottle and sank it.

Ol' John gave a despairing wail. He made one final stretch. In the same moment the wave struck the boat. Ol' John went over the side, head first.

But he was as much at home in the water as on it. In a few moments he had caught the dinghy and I was helping him climb back aboard. "Doc," he moaned, "de rum get lost. De rum get lost."

"And a good thing," I said. "Now you better get this boat under control before we all get lost."

But he was stunned by grief. He sat in the bottom of the dinghy shaking his head, moaning. Meanwhile the wind was battering the sail so I thought it would be torn to pieces. Worse, we were drifting farther and farther out to sea, but with shoals and rocks all around us. Finally I said, "If you want to drown yourself, that's your business. But I'm not going to drown with you. Now are you going to sail this boat, or am I going to take charge and sail her myself?"

He sighed. "All right, Doc. I sail her."

He did, but his heart wasn't in it any more. After a while he even consented to let me lower the mainsail and we proceeded at a more normal pace to Sweeting's Cay.

Next morning I met Charles on schedule and went with him to West Palm Beach. I got my Christmas shopping done and was back home in plenty of time for one of the most pleasant, happy Christmases I have ever spent. But after dinner that day, dozing on a full stomach, I was startled by Viola saying suddenly, "Evans! Wake up! What were you dreaming about? What made you look that way—as if you had seen a ghost?"

It was no ghost. I had just dreamed of what might have happened if I had missed connections with Charles in Sweeting's Cay. I might have had to spend Christmas with Ol' John.

28

Cutting and Sewing

A LETTER from Dr. Gottlieb said he was planning to leave on his vacation May 15; he would be glad for me to come over early, if I wished, and familiarize myself with the setup. It sounded like a chance for another of my non-regulation internships, so I wrote I would arrive shortly after the middle of April.

Since the settlement of Pine Ridge was actually two miles from the dock, and since the lumber company would be furnishing quarters for me and my family, I left the *Green Cross* in Marsh Harbour. I hired a man to keep it pumped out, to raise and dry the sails after rains, and that sort of thing. Or so I thought.

The internship worked beautifully. For two weeks I sat at Gottlieb's desk with his files and my notebook in front of me. As he examined the patients he gave me the data and I wrote them down, along with his prescription. Then I filled the prescription for him, which gave me a chance to learn his drugs. A number of these were new to me: some because they appeared under different names from the ones I knew; others were drugs with which I was not acquainted at all. Whenever something occurred which I didn't understand, I made a note of it. At the end of each day Dr. Gottlieb and I would go over these one by one. It was like a short, but intense postgraduate course and of great help to me.

And I had a real job coming up—a much bigger one than

233

I had expected. Just about the time Dr. Gottlieb left on his vacation, the lumber company signed a contract for the delivery of a vast number of pit props to mines in the British Isles. This necessitated the importation of several hundred workmen from Turks Island, Cat Island, Andros, and other places. Most of these brought families with them. In the course of a few weeks that summer my work load almost trebled.

The increase, I regret to say, was even greater than a strictly mathematical progression of possible patients would have forecast. The new workmen were housed in separate settlements; that is, the Turks Islanders in one settlement, the Cat Islanders in another, and so on. On the whole they stayed in their own towns. But now and then a Cat Island boy would fall in love with a Turks Island girl and go calling. The usual result was that I too would have to go calling, to patch up the survivors of an almost inevitable battle.

Where love failed to supply me with work, alcohol did. Particularly on Saturday afternoons and nights. The lumber company paid off at Saturday noon, and the men had the rest of the day off. The bar was handy to the paymaster's office, and equally handy to the clinic. It was the one real meeting place for men from all the islands. By 12:30 on Saturday afternoons there issued from it a soft, droning hum, as from a great swarm of flies. By 2:30 it sounded more like bees, clearly audible at the clinic a block away. By 3:30 it took on the faint rumblings of thunder. Usually by 5 the storm broke. There were screams and shouts, the lightning flash of knives or razors, and a great crowd of people would come rushing toward the clinic, bearing the victim or victims to me for repair. Quite often it developed into a kind of contest to see whether I could sew as fast as the drunks could cut.

As the Saturday nights wore on, love and alcohol combined their effects to keep me busy. There would be more than the average number of inter-village visits. Also, Saturday was the big night for wife-beating, though often these victims did not present themselves to me before Sunday morning, or even Monday, bearing bruises, cuts, sprains, and tales of woe.

234

Along with the treatment I normally threw in some free advice; namely, quit the brute. However, to the best of my knowledge, none of them ever did, except now and then to fly to the arms of some other man who beat them on the next Saturday night. So they must have liked their beatings.

Even so, every time a beaten-up wife presented herself to me, I fumed with hot but impotent indignation—particularly when it occurred in the middle of the night and I had to climb wearily out of bed to repair a broken rib or split lip. I, as well as the wife, was being victimized, and I longed for a chance to retaliate. I am happy to report that on one Saturday night the opportunity presented itself.

It had been a busy afternoon and evening, with more than the usual number of customers limping or carried in from the bar. I didn't get away from the clinic until after 11. By the time I got home and Viola had given me a bite to eat and we had gone to bed it was after midnight. Just as I was drifting to sleep the knocking started. Groaning wearily, I got up, put on a bathrobe, and went to the door.

There stood a frail little woman with both eyes so swollen they were almost shut. She was bleeding from the nose and from the mouth, from which two teeth were freshly missing. Her upper lip was cut and swollen and there were abrasions on both arms. I took one look and immediately escorted her to the clinic next door.

While I worked she told me the story. Her husband had come home drunk, a routine Saturday affair. But this time he had been sporting around with a prostitute. His wife knew it and told him so. He flew into a rage, beat her across the back with a piece of firewood (her back was a mass of bruises), knocked her down, kicked her in the face, and threatened to kill her.

As she talked I grew more and more angry, muttering to myself what ought to be done to such drunken bums. Suddenly the little woman reached up and patted me reassuringly on the shoulder. "Now, Doctuh, dot's all right. Don't you fret your-

235

self. Jus' you wait and see what I done to him. He be here soon, Doctuh."

"Here?"

"If he can make it. When he say he goin' to kill me, I jump up and run in de kitchen. He run after me and I grab up de butcher knife and when he come at me, I give it to him."

"You mean—did you kill him?"

"I ain' stay to look, Doctuh; but I ain' think so. I think he be here soon."

She was right. I was putting a final bandage on the lady when there was a knock at the door. I opened it and there stood a man with the right sleeve of his shirt gone, exposing a gash that had opened his arm from shoulder to elbow. Behind me the lady cried, "Dot's him, Doctuh! Dot's my old man!"

I looked him straight in the face, keeping him outside the door. "Well, sweet for you," I said. "It looks like you got what you deserve."

He whined, "You ain' understand, Doc. I was just scolding her, and—"

"I saw the kind of scolding you did. A little more and you'd have killed her. Now what do you want here?"

His left hand fluttered up and down the bloody arm. "You gotta do somethin' 'bout dis."

"So you want me to take care of it?" I rubbed my hands together: Shylock about to collect his pound of flesh. "Come in. I'll take care of it all right."

I have always had a great concern for the feelings of my patients. I hate to inflict pain and I am happy in alleviating it. At Pine Ridge I had earned (and, I like to think, justly) something of a reputation for extreme gentleness in the suturing of cuts. It was my custom to infiltrate thoroughly with novocaine. I would use as small a suturing needle as the circumstances would permit and sew as gently as possible. Normally the result was that the patient would feel little if any pain.

I did not consider this a normal occasion. For one thing, the brute was so well anesthetized with rum he was more aware of my expression and tone of voice than of physical pain. I swabbed iodine on the raw edges of his wound from end to end. "That'll burn," I said.

The man howled.

"Shut up!" I said. "That's what you get for kicking your wife's teeth out."

I poured sulfathiazole in the deep part of the cut, selected a large suturing needle, and threaded it carefully in front of him. "Now!" I said, and drove the needle through the flesh on both sides of the wound and pulled it tight.

"Doc!" the man screamed. "You too rash!"

"If you don't like it," I said, "go somewhere else." I stabbed the needle again. "That's what you get for beating your wife with a stick." Another stab. "That's for blacking one eye." Stab. "That's for the other." Stab. "That's for splitting her lip."

With each stab I made a comment. And after each comment his wife, standing pressed against the wall on the far side of the room, cried, "Dot's it, Doctuh! Dot's it! Fix him up!"

When I had finished the man sat with his head bent, breathing heavily. "You one rash mon, Doc."

"Come back here again," I said, "and you'll find how rash I can be. Now get out while I call the police and report this. You tried to kill your wife and you're lucky they won't be after you for murder."

As he left his wife was laughing through her bandages. "You handle him jus' right, Doctuh."

"He's still drunk," I said. "He didn't feel it as much as he should." I turned to her. "And you'd better not stay in the same house with him until he sobers up."

She chuckled. "He kill me sure if I go home tonight. I go stay wid my sister."

But just as she was leaving the police arrived. Her neighbors had already reported the fight and the husband had been picked up and jailed as he was leaving my office. "But I don't think he would have caused any more trouble tonight," the policeman said. "The fight had gone out of him. What did you do to him, Doctor?"

"I had to suture the wound in his arm. That's all."

237

The policeman shook his head. "He's been a tough one. But tonight the only thing he would say was, 'Dot doctuh one rash mon. He one rash mon.' "

I went home and to bed, weary, but with the sense of a day's work well done.

Dr. Gottlieb's vacation stretched from three months into five and it was October when he and his family finally returned. The company gave a party to welcome them home and at the same time to say farewell to the Cottmans. In the middle of the festivities the police arrived, bearing with them a man whose upper lip hung grotesquely down over his chin, attached at the top only by a narrow isthmus of skin and flesh. The two guests of honor had to excuse themselves and go sew the errant lip back into place.

It was a very odd-looking wound and I asked the man how it happened.

His speech, naturally, was a little stiff. "I kiss my wife and she bit me."

The policeman interrupted. "Don't you believe him, Doctuh. Dot ain' his wife. Dot was his sweetheart."

Whether it took place in passion or in anger I never did find out. But either way, it seemed like a fitting end for my summer's work.

29

Rickety Old Ladies

I CAN still remember, with a sense of shock, my first view of the *Green Cross* on returning to Marsh Harbour. I had left her, I thought, in good hands, and I pictured her just the way she had been.

Instead she sat low in the water, listing slightly to starboard. Her paint was flaked and gray. The furled sail looked gray and moldy. As I sculled alongside I could see that moss hung on her bottom like a grandfather's beard. When I went aboard things were even worse than they appeared from outside. The walls of the cabin were thick with mold. The bedding was moldy and rotten. The engine was frozen with rust. The whole place reeked with the odor of mold and rot. I went on deck and tried to raise the sails. They fell into shreds.

I put her ashore. There were no ways here at that time so I sailed as high on the shore as possible with a flood tide, letting her keel rest on two logs. As the tide started to ebb and the *Green Cross* to list to starboard, I pushed blocks under her bilge to hold her upright. This way she was completely out of water at low tide. I found that teredo worms had honeycombed her keel and some of the planking in the cabin had rotted.

The repairs were a long slow job, made no easier by the fact I no longer had a medical office. The house I had formerly rented had been sold. No other place was available. I was forced to store my medical equipment and drugs aboard the boat simply to have some place to keep them. And though by now I had cleaned up the mildew, the place still leaked. Drugs stored in cardboard boxes were constantly getting ruined; those in glass jars were safe enough, except the metal screw tops would rust. After one particularly heavy rain I found a whole shelf of bottles with the labels washed off, leaving me mystified as to their contents.

Something simply had to be done about an office, and Viola came up with an idea. "Why don't you," she said, "ask the Methodists if you can use the upstairs of the church?"

It seemed like a good idea. The Methodist church sat right on the bay shore, directly across the street from our house. It was just one room, twenty-four feet wide by thirty feet long. But above this was a second story. Originally it had been intended to house visiting preachers, though none had used it in many years. In fact, the 1947 hurricane (the same one I had partially slept through) had carried away the outside

239

stairs which were the only means of reaching the second floor. After that someone had climbed up, somehow, and nailed the door shut. And so it had remained.

Now I asked and got permission to use the second floor temporarily as an office.

The first problem was to get in, and at this point I began to wonder who had nailed that upper door shut, and how. In all Marsh Harbour there were only three ladders. Two were too short. The third was long enough, but when I stepped on the first rung the entire ladder collapsed.

I sent to Nassau for two long pieces of two-by-four and made a ladder of my own. Then, armed with a wrecking bar and hammer, I climbed up and forced an entrance. The room was big and dark. There were windows but they were shuttered and these had to be pried open. When light finally poured in I saw the room was the same size as the church below. It was furnished with a table, two chairs (one of them broken), a pitcher, and a wash basin. Consequently, when I brought in my drugs and books there was no place to put them except on the floor. On the other hand, there was ample floor space.

And so, in the early part of 1953, there began for me an eight-month period of medical practice flavored and spiced with Methodism. Sunday mornings are usually rather busy times for a Marsh Harbour doctor, but because of the location of my office I tried not to practice during church hours. One Sunday, however, I had hurried to my office to get some drugs before services started. It was a dark morning with rain threatening. Something delayed me, and before I could leave the congregation had assembled. Rather than disturb the meeting by appearing outside the window on my ladder, I sat quietly and waited. What with my far-flung medical calls it had been quite some time since I had been to church, and I was sure that Viola, who attended regularly, would think it good for me.

There was a hymn and an opening prayer. The sounds coming up through the thin floor into the big, empty room seemed to vibrate all around me. The lay preacher that morning was

240

a venerable gentleman named Captain Bobby Archer, a former sea captain. He was a very tall, dignified old man with white hair and a somewhat quavery voice. "I have taken my text," he announced, his voice rolling softly up to where I sat, "from the ninety-third Psalm." He paused. I could visualize him opening his Bible. "The Lord reigneth," he pronounced, and paused again.

And at that precise moment the Lord did indeed open the heavens and rain over land and sea with great violence. In fact, the rain beat on the roof so hard it drowned out most of the sounds from below and I couldn't tell whether or not anyone in the congregation noticed this bit of heavenly humor. But knowing how serious and somber Abaco folk are regarding their religion, I made a small bet with myself they had not. To check I asked one of my Methodist patients that afternoon if she had noticed just when the rain started. "No," she said. "Except it was early in the service. Why?"

"I was just wondering," I said, and silently paid myself off.

The big problem with my new office was how to get the patients in and out, particularly the old ladies. Many of them put very little faith in my ladder, and to tell the truth I could scarcely blame them. I stanchioned it as best I could, but it seemed possessed of a dinghylike demon. It would slip away from the stanchions, slide about, wobble and twist under the weight of anyone climbing it.

I remember in particular one feeble old lady who was coming to me for a series of treatments. She had trouble walking at best and was always accompanied by her daughter. But when she arrived at the bottom of the ladder it was, I thought (influenced by my surroundings), like the door to the Judgment Room: she had to go it alone. The ladder was too narrow for two persons, and too weak.

The first time she came, her daughter stood at the foot of the ladder and boosted her mother slowly upward. I lay flat on my belly at the top of the ladder, head and shoulders hanging out the door, and reached downward—extending in true

241

Methodist fashion the right hand of fellowship. But there was still a hiatus of some six feet between her and my outstretched hand.

"Put your foot on the next step, Mama," her daughter said. Cautiously, Mama complied. "Now pull yourself up."

She pulled. The ladder wavered. Mama screamed. My heart was in my mouth, well out over the doorsill. I swallowed it back into place. "Now, Mrs. Romer," I said, "there's nothing to be afraid of. I'm holding the top of the ladder. It can't slip."

She made it another step. This got her too high for the daughter to reach, and now the daughter panicked. "Mama!" she screamed. "You going to fall! Come down, Mama!"

"I can't!" the old lady wailed.

"Mrs. Romer," I said. "Please. And you shut up, Miss Romer. Now, raise your hand, Mrs. Romer."

That advice was no good. She was clutching the ladder with both hands and had no intention of turning loose.

"All right," I said. "Wait. Wait just a moment." I had some rope in the office. Quickly I tied a noose in one end and lowered it to her. "Now slip that around you and I can pull you up."

Instead she merely grabbed the rope with one hand. Yet the touch of it seemed to give her not only confidence but the agility of a squirrel. She practically sprinted up the rest of the way and through the door.

Her heartbeat was rapid that day and her blood pressure high, which I considered normal under the circumstances. But when it was time to go back down the ladder she put the rope around her and in complete confidence shinnied back to earth.

It gave me an idea. Next morning I rigged up a block and tackle over my doorway. Whenever timid, frail, or rickety old ladies arrived, I came down and tied the rope under their arms. Then as they climbed I helped them along with a boost for every step. None of them ever fell off the ladder; but if they had, they would have remained suspended in mid-air and I could have raised or lowered them according to their preference.

30

The Old Order Changeth

ONE of the reasons I had so much trouble finding an office that fall of 1952 was that the postwar economic boom sweeping the United States had suddenly reached out and clutched Marsh Harbour to its bosom. An American industrialist, one Mr. J. B. Crockett, had visited the place and decided its weather was perfect for large-scale farming. The soil was poor, but it would serve as a base for fertilizer. Mr. Crockett leased several thousand acres. Almost overnight he brought in bulldozers and other giant, weirdly shaped pieces of machinery that swept the land clean and planted it in bananas, papaws, and avocado pears. Machine shops, warehouses, and docks began to sprout like birdgrass all over the place. And everybody who wanted one, or even would allow one to be forced on him, had a job.

As a result, prosperity bloomed in Marsh Harbour like spring flowers in the desert. Stores which had once stocked only grits and sugar now had their shelves piled high with goods. People began to buy radios, new clothes, new furniture. Private Delco light plants spread, and there was talk of a public power system sometime in the future. This led to electric lights and refrigerators. And the streets, about ten feet wide where they existed at all, were suddenly jammed with trucks and jeeps belonging to Mr. Crockett's farm, half of them, usually, stopped in pull-offs to allow the other half to get by.

It was not an unmixed blessing. People no longer sauntered, pausing to gossip beneath the mango and avocado trees. The shade on the shore where the Job's Comforters had sat while the *Green Cross* was being built was empty. In fact, there wasn't even time for boat-building any more. People were too busy driving trucks and leaping out of the way of bulldozers.

It was at this point I decided, with my usual sense of timing, to build my dream house atop the great bluff I had bought from Dr. Stratton. The only help I could hire was that which Mr. Crockett's farms would not hire, and they would hire anything with one hand, one foot, and an I.Q. of fifty. Consequently my house was largely a do-it-yourself project. Compared to my problems, Mr. Blanding's Dream House was a prefabricated affair put up in a couple of hours one Saturday afternoon. My house, believe it or not, took just over seven years to finish.

Meanwhile, of course, my work as a doctor went on. Otherwise, even under those circumstances I might have finished a bit sooner. I did, in fact, get an office—a small, square, concrete building in what was to be the backyard of the new house—built by the fall of 1953, and moved my work into it. After that, instead of rushing all the way from my hilltop to the attic of the Methodist church, I had merely to rush from the roof of one building down to the other.

Even so, my patients were always arriving at the most inopportune of times: just when I had the cement mixed and was about to begin pouring; or just as I had a frame up that had to be held in place until it was fastened. On the other hand, there were certain advantages. To fit its surroundings my house was designed to look like a castle. Perched high among its turrets and battlements, I could usually see my patients approaching from afar, toiling wearily up the bluff and probably deciding never to go to a doctor again. So I would try, where possible, to time my work to fit their arrival.

This did particularly well in the case of one lady who was coming to me twice a week for a series of injections. She came by boat from Man-o'-War Harbour four miles away. From my lookout I could usually spot her boat the moment she put out of the harbor. I would continue work until she was within a quarter mile of the shore. Then I would climb down, grab my syringe, and rush down the hill. As the boat came in I would wade knee-deep into the sea. The lady would hang her arm over the gunwale. As the boat stopped, down went the needle. As the needle came out her husband would turn the boat. And I would head back up the bluff.

In order to get supplies from the town to my slowly budding castle I bought a half-ton Willys truck. In it I was driving home from work one day when I saw a couple on the road ahead of me. They both wore shorts and shirts that were soaking wet. When I asked if they wanted a ride they happily climbed in.

The man introduced himself as a Mr. Westphal and told me they were off a boat anchored in Boat Harbour. They were on their way to town for supplies, and since they did not tow a dinghy it had been necessary to swim ashore. When I made some remark about the difficulties of sailing without a dinghy he said, "Oh, my wife is quite a sailor. You may have heard of her. She writes books under the name of Ann Davison."

It is a wonder I didn't run the truck in a ditch. Because I had read and heard a great deal about Ann Davison, the only woman in the world who had navigated the Atlantic Ocean alone in a twenty-three-foot sailboat. Sometimes, wrestling the *Green Cross* through the Bahamas, I had mused on the exploits of Ann Davison the way a young, would-be pianist, fumbling awkwardly through the scales, might ponder on Paderewski. But now in the flesh she did not look the way I had imagined her. She was slender, about forty, with blonde, rather flaxen hair and a pleasant face. A friendly face, without pretense.

I asked how long they were going to be on Abaco and she said, "For quite a while possibly. I wonder if you could tell me the best way to get from Boat Harbour around to Marsh Harbour. I understand the channel is tricky."

"I'll be happy to pilot you," I said. And then I started to laugh: me piloting the only woman who had navigated the Atlantic Ocean alone! If only Job's Comforters had been still sitting under their shade on the shore so I could tell them.

Anyway, I went over the next morning and climbed aboard the *Felicity Ann*. Though I had read about this boat I was still amazed at its smallness. Twenty-three feet over all, it was correspondingly narrow. Alongside her, the *Green Cross* was a Leviathan. Inside the cabin there was no standing room except at the hatch, and then only when it was open. But despite her size she was a deep-draft boat with a five-foot keel and she sailed beautifully.

The trip to Marsh Harbour that morning took about two hours. In that time I found Ann Davison to be one of the most congenial, sparkling, and witty persons I had ever met. I had come loaded with questions I wanted to ask, and she answered them freely. Even so, I realized after a while that I was the one being most drawn out. Ann had that rare trait of being both a good talker and a good listener. She could ask just the right question at the right time to make a person feel she was sincerely interested, not merely being polite. By the time we sailed into Marsh Harbour I found I had told her a good bit about my life in the out-islands.

"Doctor," she said, "you can't let that wonderful material just die. You simply must write it down."

Somewhat embarrassed, I admitted to having kept diaries and having made a tentative start on a book.

"I'd love to see it, and the diaries. I promise to take good care of them."

It was the start of a warm friendship that has endured. And it is in large measure due to the encouragement and help that Ann Davison gave me that I am finally getting all this down on paper. Even after she and her husband left Marsh Harbour we kept in touch, and from time to time she would write urging me to go ahead with my project and giving suggestions as to how to proceed.

Meanwhile the Abaco boom had kept right on booming. Mr. Crockett subleased his holdings to the S & M Farms, a big agricultural syndicate. It expanded the work, built big loading docks, brought in more labor from Haiti and from other islands in the Bahamas. Also, the Owens-Illinois Company that op-

246

erated the great lumber company where Dr. Gottlieb worked at Pine Ridge had by now cut most of the timber on Grand Bahama. Plans were made to move to Snake Cay, which is on Abaco, just ten miles from Marsh Harbour. Docks were built there; houses were built and other houses brought in ready-built to shelter the incoming workers. A road was cut to Marsh Harbour; other roads began to push out into the timber north and south.

All this, but no new doctor. Dr. Gottlieb was still on Grand Bahama and would be until the final move of Owens-Illinois. Dr. Stratton was gone now a good part of the time. I was alone, and swamped with work. I worked day and night. I had to move my office once more, back from the bluff into the town.

But eventually Owens-Illinois moved their headquarters to Abaco, and with that came Dr. Gottlieb and his clinic. There was an immediate lightening of the load I had been carrying.

I was glad indeed to have it so. Years before I had quit teaching school to seek a slower, more leisurely and romantic life. I had chosen a land rich in natural beauty; I had acquired one of the most superb views to be found in all these fabulous islands—or anywhere else for that matter. My dream castle was finally finished—well, almost finished; dream castles can never be quite complete. I had done all this, but in the last few years I had somehow got too buried in work to profit by it—to profit truly in the sense of full enjoyment.

My work had been important, yes. I had ministered to the sick to the best of my ability; I had relieved some pain and suffering; in some cases I have even saved lives. I was proud of the work, truly proud, and proud of the friends I had made, both white and colored.

But I was happy to see Dr. Gottlieb arrive and relieve me of some of the burden.

Because there are still a lot of things I want to do. For one thing, there are still a lot of out-islands, untouched by lumber companies and industrial concerns, but in range of a sailboat. So after Gottlieb's arrival I would work in my office only mornings and evenings. Each afternoon I would climb into one of the high turrets of my castle and pull up the trap door (I actually have one) after me. My office in Marsh Harbour is small and frequently hot, but the castle is always windswept. I remember how it was that first time I stepped into the shade of a fig tree on Crooked Island and found it was like stepping from broiling sunlight into an air-conditioned room, only one air-conditioned by nature herself. It is always like that up here. It is conducive to work. And also to dreams and new plans—and I have been cooking up some very intriguing ones for the future. They may or may not work out, but somehow I have managed before to see daydreams take form and substance.

I am very content at the moment, pausing as I work on this last paragraph, to look out the casement at the magnificent panorama of land, sea, and sky, framed by the great pillars of my portico. I can see Gayle playing on our beach, and downstairs Viola is working on new curtains for our living room. My mind wanders back to the opening scene of this story of mine and the announcement of the constable as we paraded the street of True Blue: "De doctuh done reach." Yes, indeed. I've "reached" and found a measure of contentment.

At least until these new plans of mine . . .